CW00427925

SUCCESSFUL WARMUPS, BOOK 2

By Nancy Telfer

ISBN 0-8497-4178-5

CONTENTS **Page**

Tips — Posture
Reminders — Breathing

Making the Most of Your Warmups:

1) Always warm up your voice before or at the beginning of a rehearsal.
2) Start with the first five warmups in this book (1a to 1e). Use these five for one week. Then omit Warmup 1a and add Warmup 2. Each week continue to omit the oldest warmup and add the next new one so that you always have five warmups to practice. Each warmup lasts five weeks.
3) Use the tips to make the most of each warmup.
4) At the end of each week, check off the warmups you have been using:

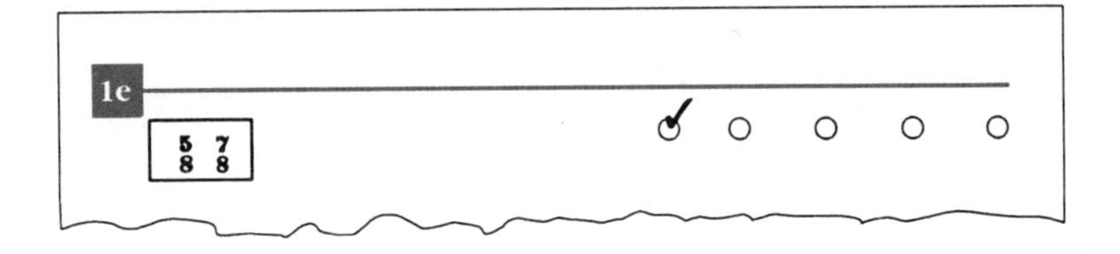
1e
5 7
8 8

Then circle the appropriate numbers on the progress chart.

5) If you are eager to improve in some specific area, check the index for appropriate warmups.

Soloists: In warmups with more than one vocal part, you may choose the part with the best range for your voice or change the key.

Men's, Women's and Children's Choirs: See the Conductor's Edition for special instructions.

Third Year

To find one's voice is a joy. But as you can hear it grow and mature, the delights are multiplied a hundredfold.

SINGERS IN POSITION

Singing in a choir is like preparing for the Olympics. The voice and the body must be trained; the mind must learn to be alert to the possibilities of music-making. When singers are in good shape, they can do almost anything with their voices.

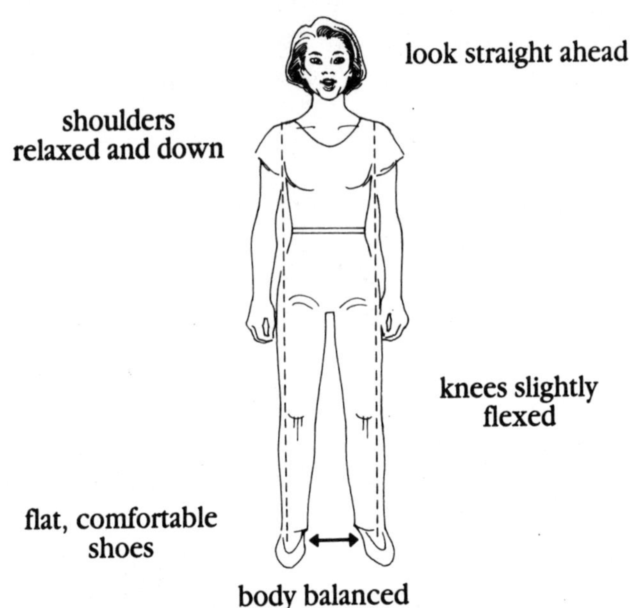
Stand like an athlete:
look straight ahead
shoulders relaxed and down
knees slightly flexed
flat, comfortable shoes
body balanced
(ready for anything)

This is the position of strength and flexibility.

1a

gentle warmup

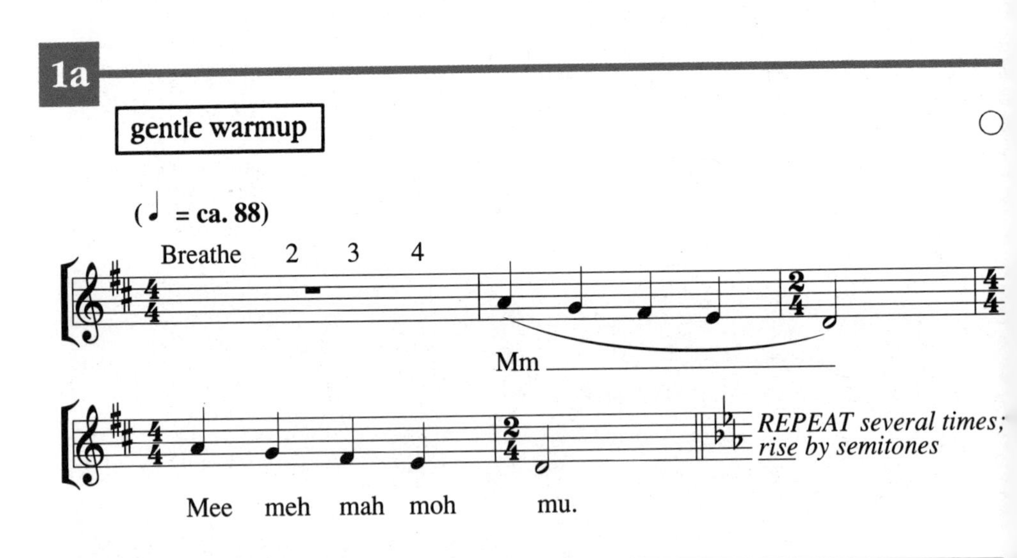
(♩ = ca. 88)
Breathe 2 3 4
Mm
Mee meh mah moh mu.
REPEAT several times;
rise by semitones

TIPS

A. Breathe quietly through your mouth.

B. Let the resonance of each "m" go forward into the vowel to make the tone richer.

1b

different phrase lengths

○ ○

Slowly (♩ = 72)

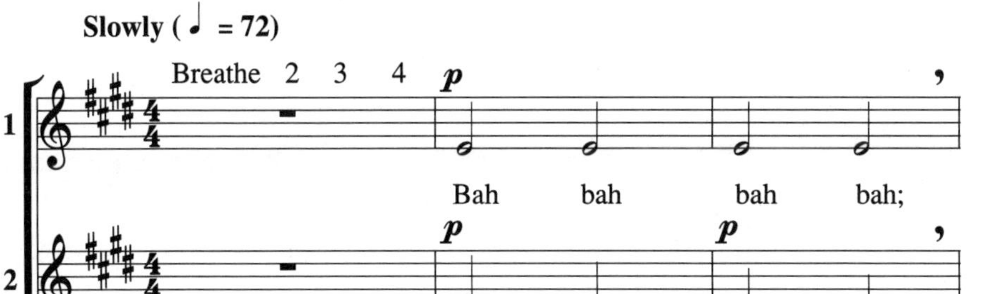
Breathe 2 3 4
Part 1
p
Bah bah bah bah;
Part 2
p
p
Bah bah bah bah;

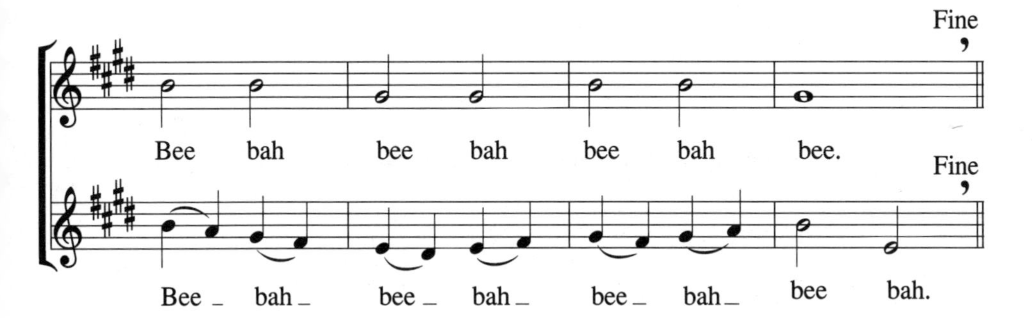
Fine
Bee bah bee bah bee bah bee.
Fine
Bee _ bah _ bee _ bah _ bee _ bah _ bee bah.

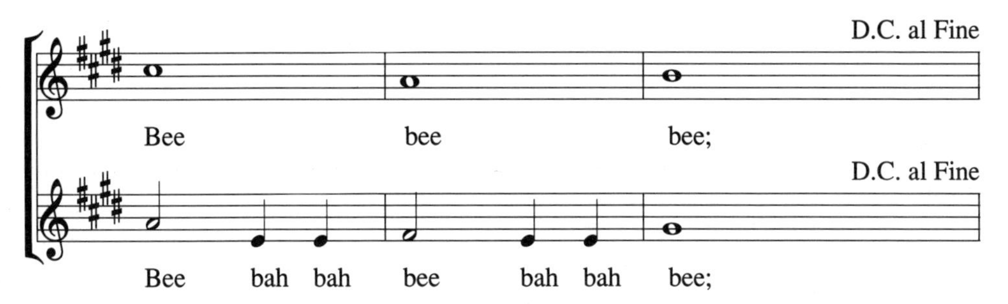
D.C. al Fine
Bee bee bee;
D.C. al Fine
Bee bah bah bee bah bah bee;

TIPS

A. Open your mouth north/south. Smile with your eyes, not your mouth.

B. Look ahead in the music to pace yourself.

C. Sing *legato*. During each phrase, imagine the rich sound flowing steadily from your mouth to the other side of the room.

1c

slurs

(𝅗𝅥 = 63)
Breathe 2
Nah ______ nah, nah_ nah_ nah_ nah;

Noh ______ noh, noh_ noh_ noh_ noh;
REPEAT, rising by semitones (alternate "nah" and "noh")

TIPS

A. To brighten the tone, show more of your two top front teeth.

B. In some types of music, you need to relax the dynamics on the second of each pair of notes.

nah_ nah_

C. For *piano*, inhale lightly.

1d

resonance on low pitches

"wz" sounds like "wizz" without the vowel

(♩ = ca. 76)
mf
Z ______
wz wz wz wz wz wz wz wz wz wz wz wz wz.

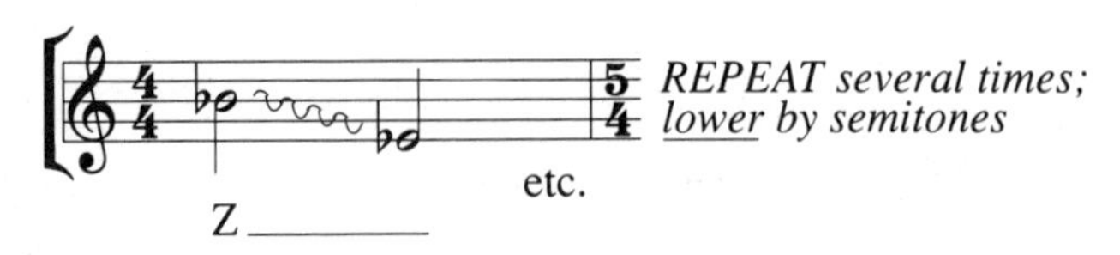
REPEAT several times; lower by semitones
etc.
Z ______

TIPS

A. Feel your tongue and teeth vibrate with each "z."

B. Give your lips a workout on the "wz."

C. If possible, stand on a hard surface (not carpet) for better resonance.

1e

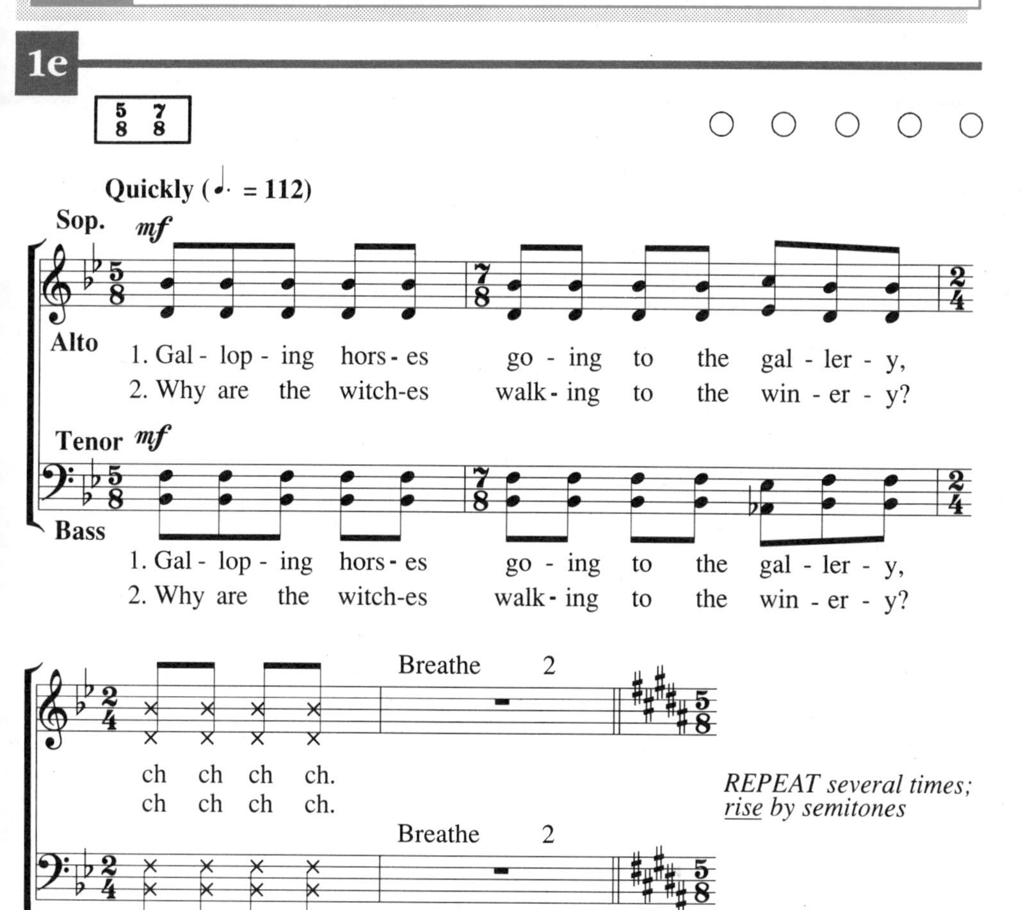
5/8 7/8
Quickly (♩. = 112)
Sop.
mf
Alto
1. Gal - lop - ing hors - es go - ing to the gal - ler - y,
2. Why are the witch-es walk - ing to the win - er - y?
Tenor
mf
Bass
1. Gal - lop - ing hors - es go - ing to the gal - ler - y,
2. Why are the witch-es walk - ing to the win - er - y?
Breathe 2
ch ch ch ch.
ch ch ch ch.
REPEAT several times; rise by semitones
Breathe 2
ch ch ch ch.
ch ch ch ch.

TIPS

A. Form the consonants clearly at the front of your mouth.

B. Good diction means:

- **Pure vowels;**
- **Distinct consonants;**
- **Appropriate emphasis on important syllables.**

C. Drink plenty of water every day. Bring your sports bottle to choir. Avoid ice water before singing.

D. For a dry mouth in concert, place the tip of your tongue against the roof of your mouth during the rests.

BREATHING

Singers should wear clothing which is not too restrictive at the waist, the ribs or the throat:

Let your spine lengthen as you inhale:

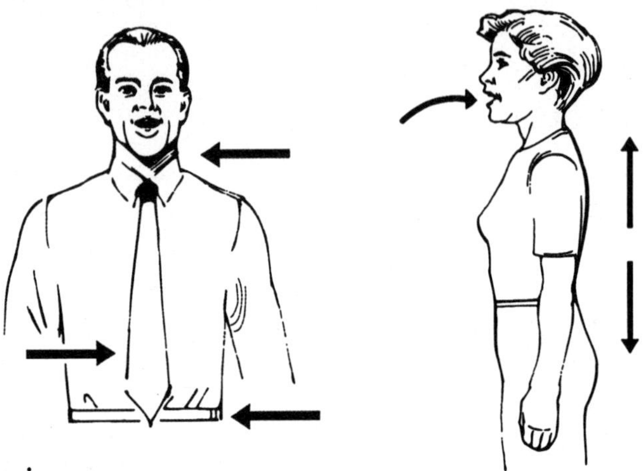

For concert music:

A. Whenever possible, breathe early in rhythm in the style of the music. Be poised to sing your best from the first note of the first entry.
B. Mark the breathing places in each piece.

2

ī

○ ○ ○ ○ ○

ī = long i
= a diphthong made from two sounds:
ah + ee

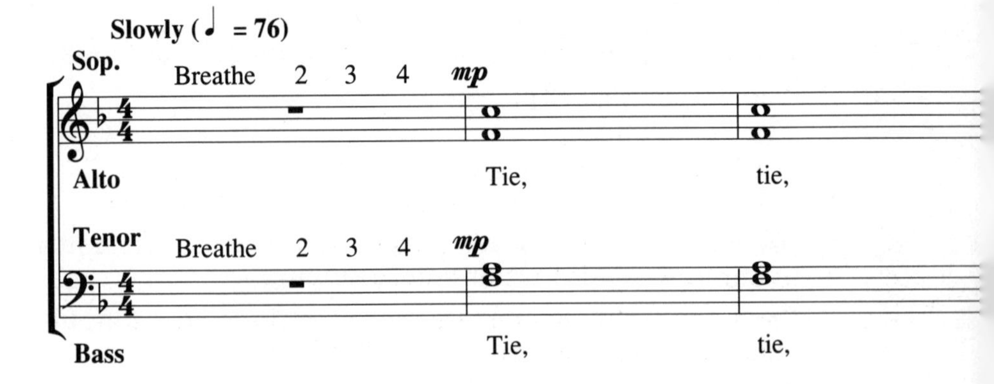
Slowly (♩ = 76)
Sop.
Alto
Tenor
Bass
Breathe 2 3 4
mp
Tie,
tie,

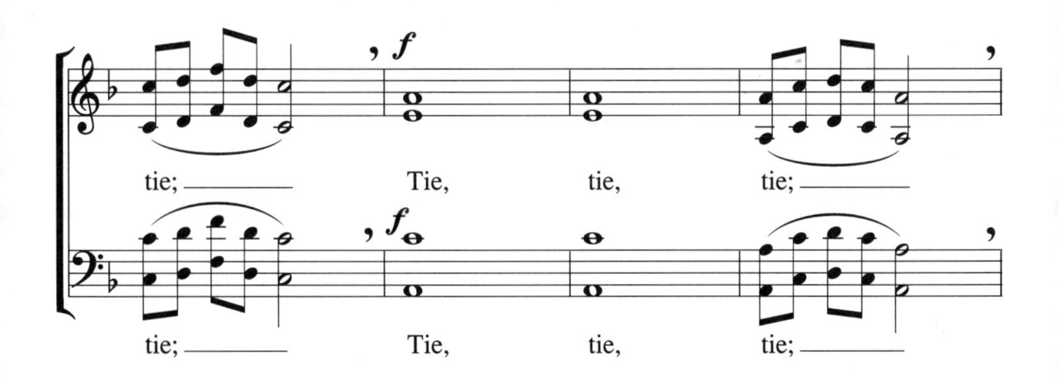
f
tie;
Tie,
tie,
tie;
f
tie;
Tie,
tie,
tie;

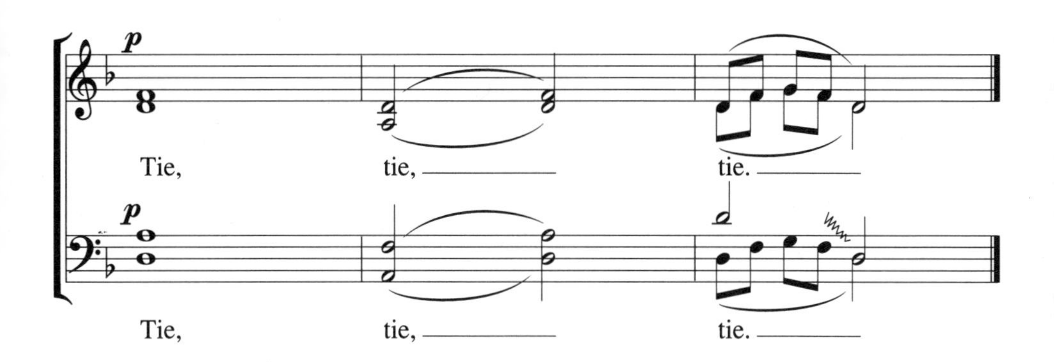
p
Tie,
tie,
tie.
p
Tie,
tie,
tie.

TIPS

A. Stretch out the "ah." Add the "ee" at the last possible moment:

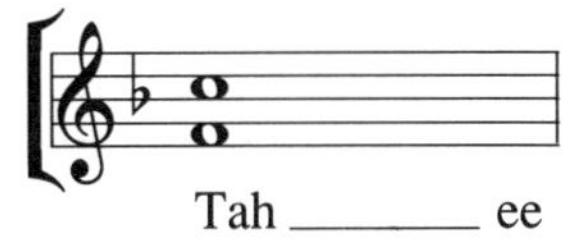
Tah
ee

Sing the "ee" lightly without emphasis.

B. If you are emphasizing the "ee" too much, try using "ah" + short "i."

3

tuning semi-tones

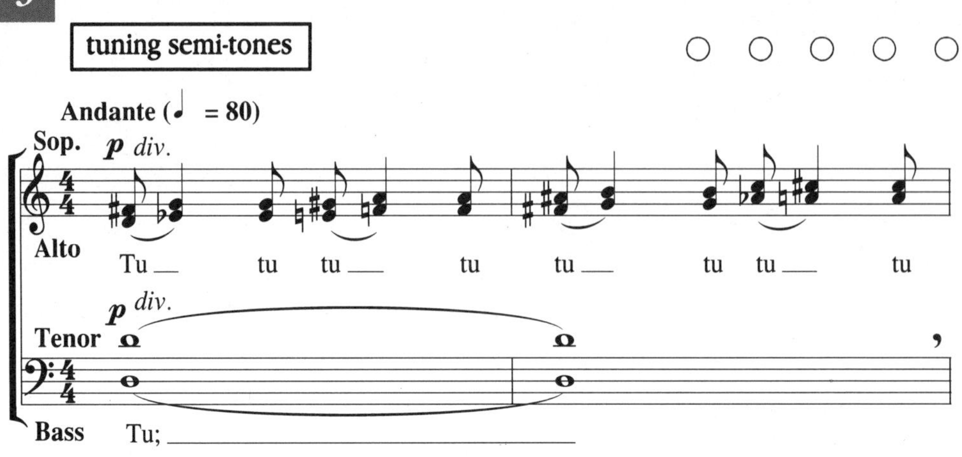
Andante (♩ = 80)
Sop.
p div.
Alto
Tu tu tu tu tu tu tu tu
p div.
Tenor
Bass
Tu;

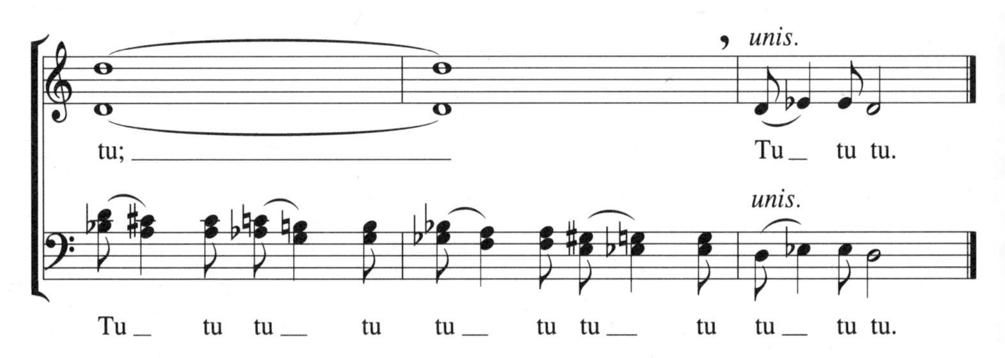
unis.
tu;
Tu tu tu.
unis.
Tu tu tu tu tu tu tu tu tu tu tu.

TIPS

A. Leave no spaces between the notes. A space interrupts the rhythms.

B. When you hear yourself out of tune, automatically sing more softly and listen carefully.

C. Imagine the tone of the vowel as you breathe in so that your mouth will be in position for the first sound.

4
sixteenth notes
(♩ = 76)
Part 1
mf
Part 2
Ee
eh

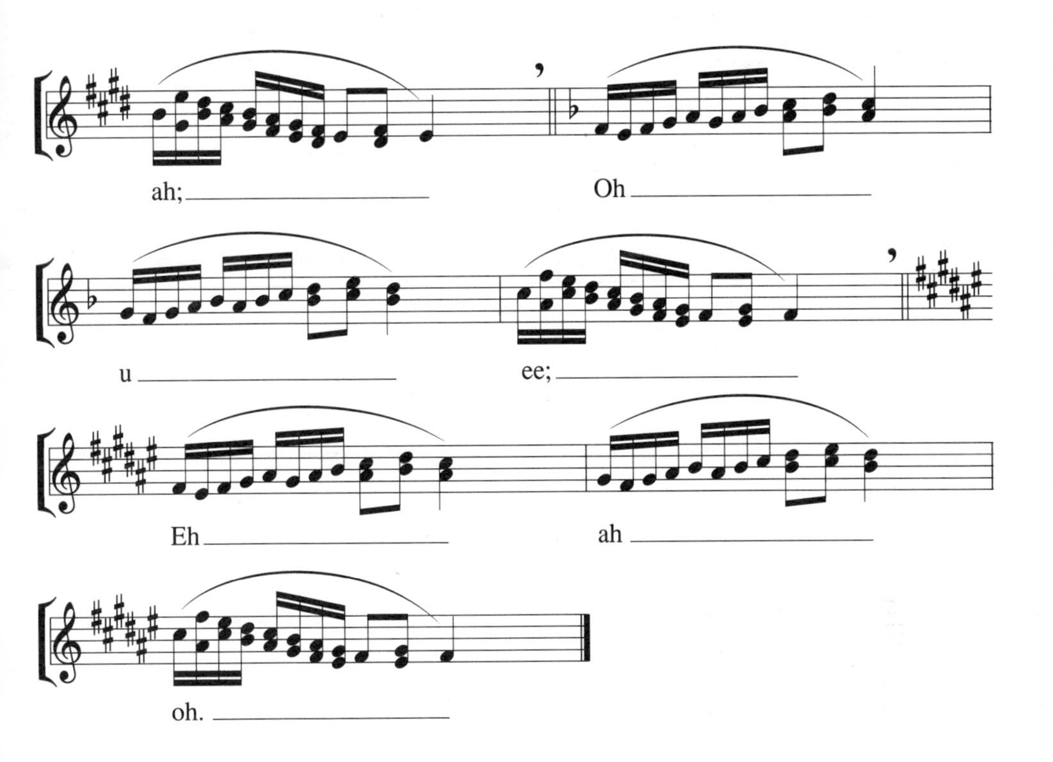
ah;
Oh
u
ee;
Eh
ah
oh.

TIPS

A. For better clarity:

1. Articulate each note separately with a "d":

Dee dee dee dee. . .
Deh deh deh deh. . .

2. Articulate each group of sixteenth notes:

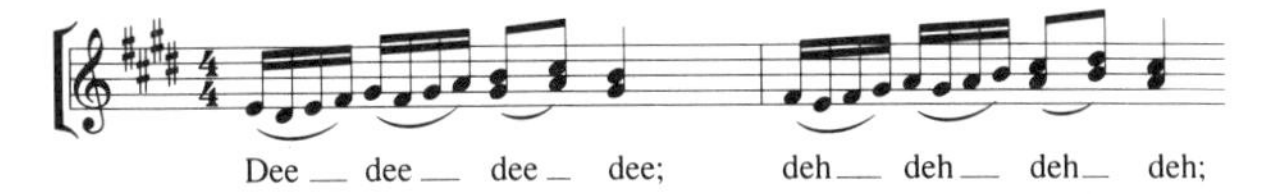
Dee dee dee dee;
deh deh deh deh;

Bounce each note slightly with the tummy. Do not leave a space between the notes (e.g. no staccato).

3. Sing the warmup as written. Continue to bounce the sixteenth notes. Do not start each note with an "h."

B. Keep the momentum moving toward the climax of each bar; then relax slightly.

SINGERS IN POSITION

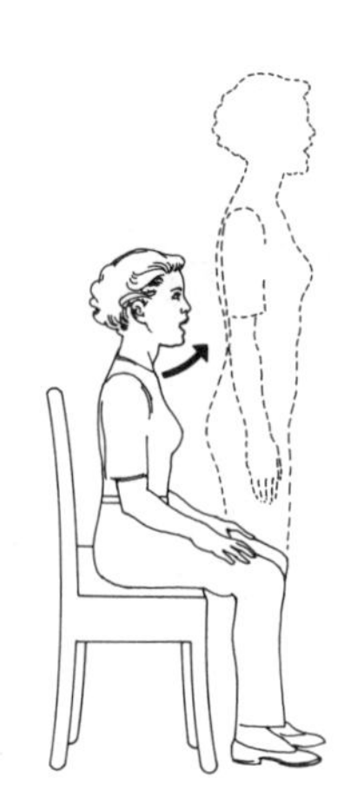

Sit in a position which makes you ready to stand up with one flowing movement. Practice moving from a sitting to a standing position several times. Pretend you are seated during a concert. Stand silently.

5

glides for consistent tone

Largo (♩ = 52)
Sop. & Ten.
unis. mp
Ah
Ah
Alto & Bass
unis. mp
Ah
Ah
Ah

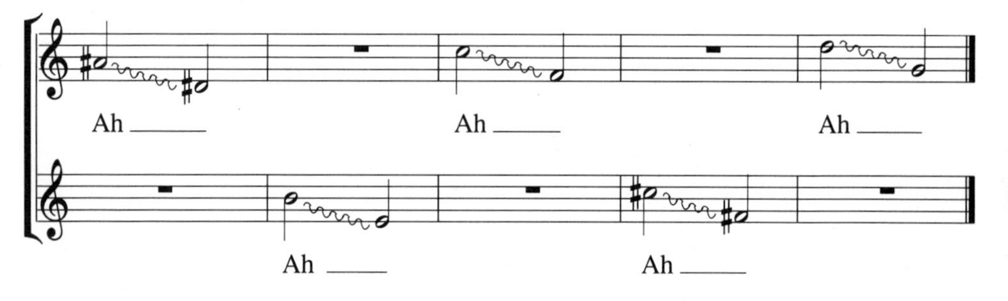

Ah
Ah
Ah
Ah
Ah

TIPS

A. Glide very slowly to the next pitch. Smooth out the sound in the areas where the voice tends to "skip" rather than move in a continuous glide.

B. Breathe in slowly to expand the throat while the other vocal part is singing.

6

continuing the idea through the rests

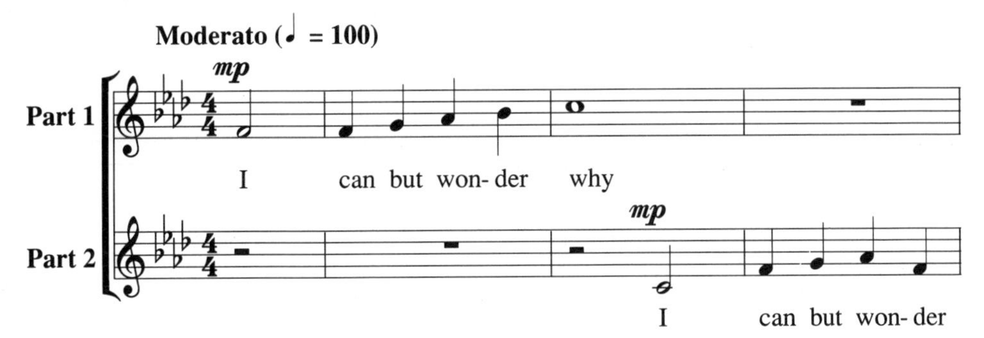
Moderato (♩ = 100)
mp
Part 1
I can but won- der why
mp
Part 2
I can but won- der

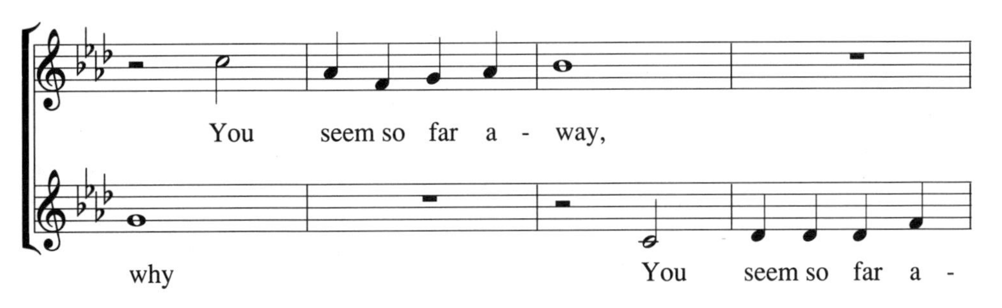
You seem so far a - way,
why
You seem so far a -

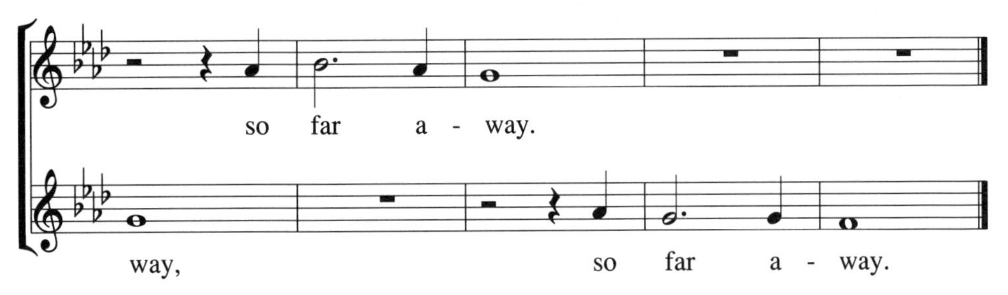
so far a - way.
way,
so far a - way.

TIPS

A. In some music, the end of the phrase seems to continue on after the singer is finished. Do not make the ending of each phrase sound "final."

B. Imagine that the voice continues on after the cut-off, but is invisible.

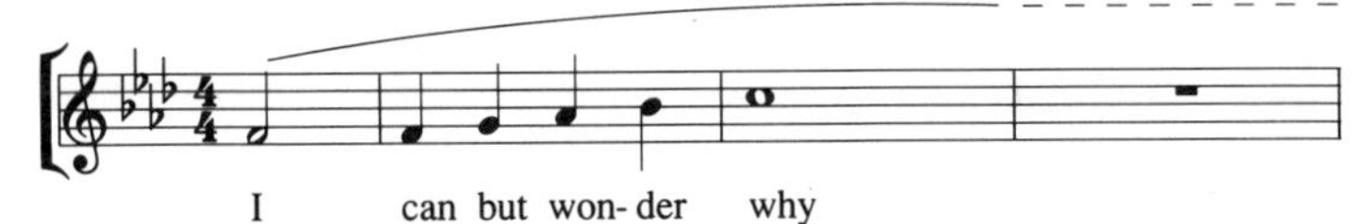
I can but won- der why

C. In some music, the entries should be very definite, but in other music, the entries should just be a continuation of the music already in progress.

7

staccato

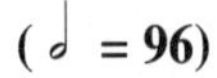
(= 96)

mp
1
2
3

1. Ah ah ah ah ah ah ah ah ah ah ah ah ah ah. Ee
2. Oh oh oh oh oh oh oh oh oh oh oh oh oh oh. U
3. Jack Sprat could eat no fat, no fat; Jack Sprat could eat no fat. Jack

ee ee ee ee ee ee ee ee ee ee ee ee ee.
u u u u u u u u u u u u u.
Sprat could eat no fat; Jack Sprat could eat no fat, no fat.

TIPS

A. Let your tummy give a little bounce for each staccato note.

B. Keep your throat completely relaxed.

C. Use lighter bounces from your tummy for short notes or a faster tempo.

8

tuning harmonically

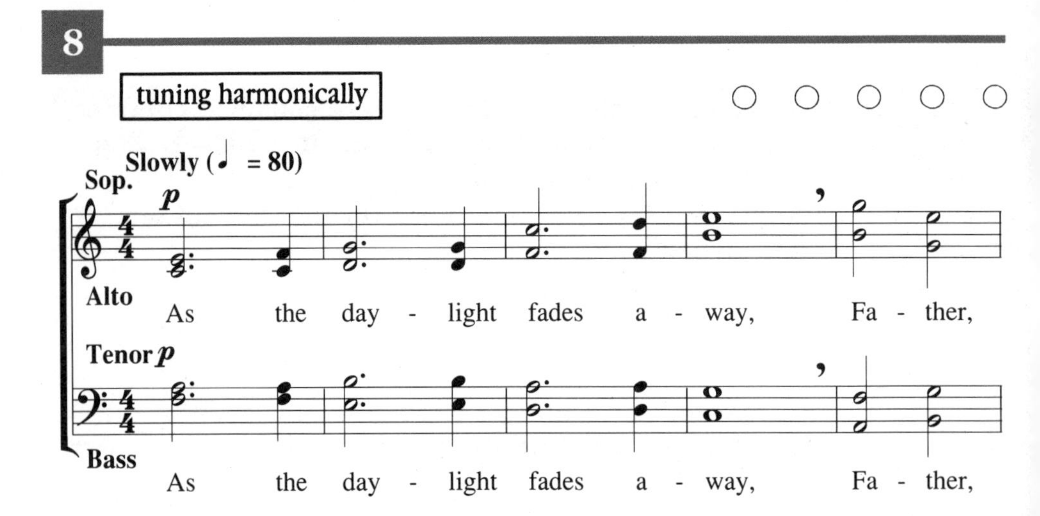
Slowly (= 80)
Sop.
p
Alto
As the day - light fades a - way, Fa - ther,
Tenor p
Bass
As the day - light fades a - way, Fa - ther,

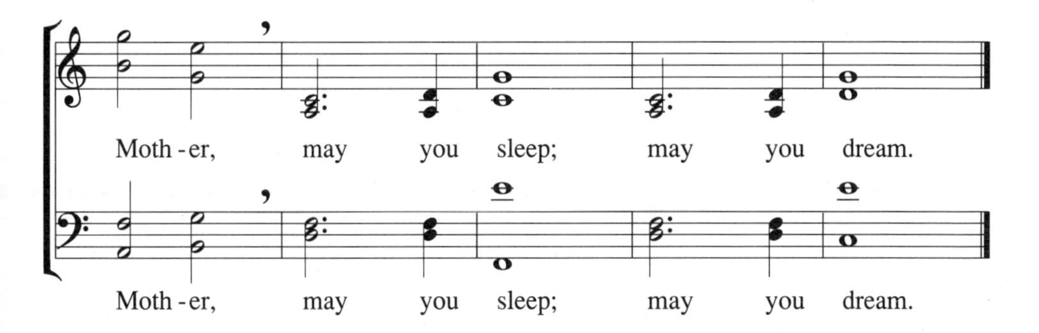
Moth - er, may you sleep; may you dream.
Moth - er, may you sleep; may you dream.

TIPS

A. When everyone sings the vowels correctly, the tuning clarifies.

B. If the "ee" or "eh" is too harsh or sharp, relax your tongue.

C. Balance your tuning with the rest of the choir.

D. If you cannot hear your own voice very well in the choir:

- **Feel how the vibrations fit with the other voices;**
- **Focus your tone more.**

Every singer is important in the choir; every voice makes a difference.

SINGERS IN POSITION

Use your energy efficiently!

Do not use an overloaded choir folder for rehearsal or concert:

- For rehearsals, hold one piece at a time.
- For dress rehearsals, practice with some music in your folder so that you are comfortable with the weight of the music.
- For concerts, place the first half of the music in your folder until intermission; then replace this with the second half of the music.

Hold your book with your elbows slightly forward to raise your ribcage for better breathing. Lower the music whenever you are not singing.

9

resonance

(♩ = 80)
Sop.
mf
Alto
Tenor
Bass
Num num num num, num num num num, num num num num, nah;
Num num num num, num num num num, num num num num, nah; etc.
(cont'd.)

TIP **For a quick warmup, use as much "m" as possible to create a big buzz around the lips and nose.**

internal "r"

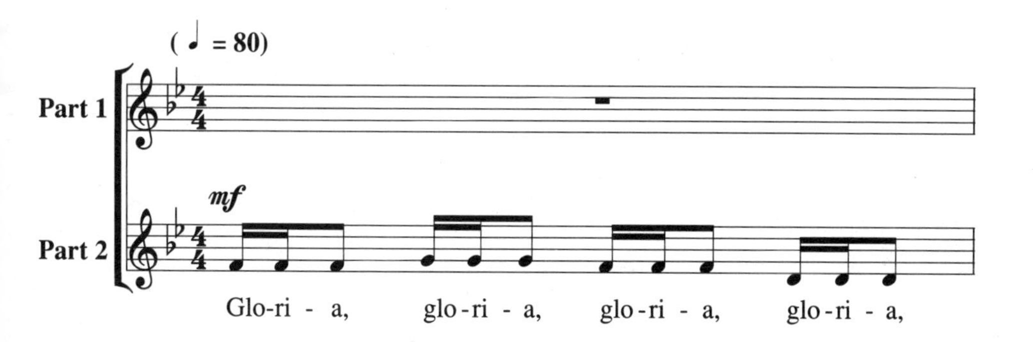
(♩ = 80)
Part 1
Part 2
mf
Glo-ri - a, glo - ri - a, glo - ri - a, glo - ri - a,

mf
Glo-ri- a, glo-ri- a, glo-ri -a, glo-ri- a, glo - ri - a.
glo - ri - a.
Glo-ri- a, glo-ri- a, glo-ri -a.
Glo-ri- a De - o,
Glo-ri- a De - o.
Glo-ri- a De - o.

TIP When an "r" comes in the middle of a word, flip the "r" very lightly with the front of your tongue. Some singers may have to use a gentle "d" on the tip of their tongue instead.

REMINDER The warmup is one of the most important parts of a rehearsal. Do not just "sing along" with the warmup. Give your voice a good workout.

11

short "e i u"

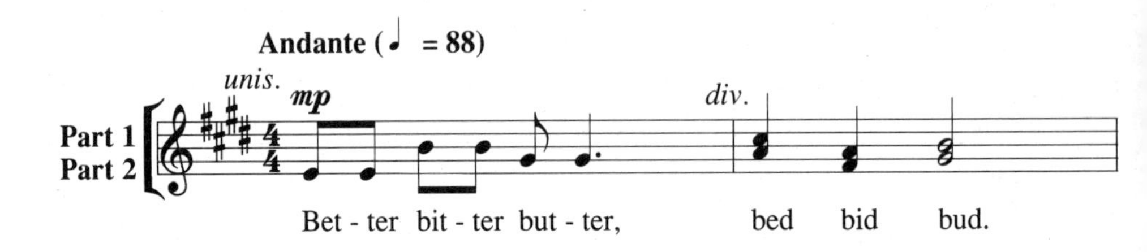
Andante (♩ = 88)
unis.
mp
div.
Part 1
Part 2
Bet - ter bit - ter but - ter, bed bid bud.

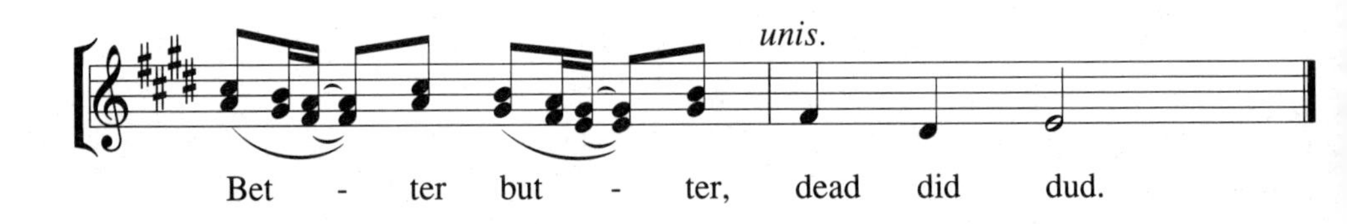
unis.
Bet - ter but - ter, dead did dud.

TIPS

A. Place the lips very slightly forward for each short vowel.

B. Short vowels do not naturally sound as full as long vowels. Concentrate on making each vowel as rich as possible.

C. For higher pitches, drop the jaw more for a mature tone.

D. When a short "u" is sung on a slur or a long note, sing "ah."

REMINDER

Be kind to your voice. Avoid speaking loudly, yelling, screaming and clearing your throat.

12

forte and piano

○ ○ ○ ○ ○

Moderato (♩ = 116)
unis. f
Part 1
Part 2
Ky - ri - e, Ky - ri - e, Ky - ri - e,
p div. f
Ky-ri - e. Ky-ri - e e - le - i - son;
p f
Ky-ri - e e - le - i - son. Chri - ste e - le - i -
p
son; Chri - ste e - le - i - son.

TIPS

A. If you slow down when you switch from loud to soft in your concert music, mark a reminder in the music:

f
p
Ky - ri - e, Ky - ri - e, Ky - ri-e, Ky-ri-e.

B. Imagine *forte* as a large picture with vibrant details.

***Piano* is the same picture reduced. The details are just as vibrant as for *forte*.**

C. Be careful with the tuning whenever the dynamics change.

13

thr str spl

ĭ = short "i"
ă = short "a"
ŏ = short "o"

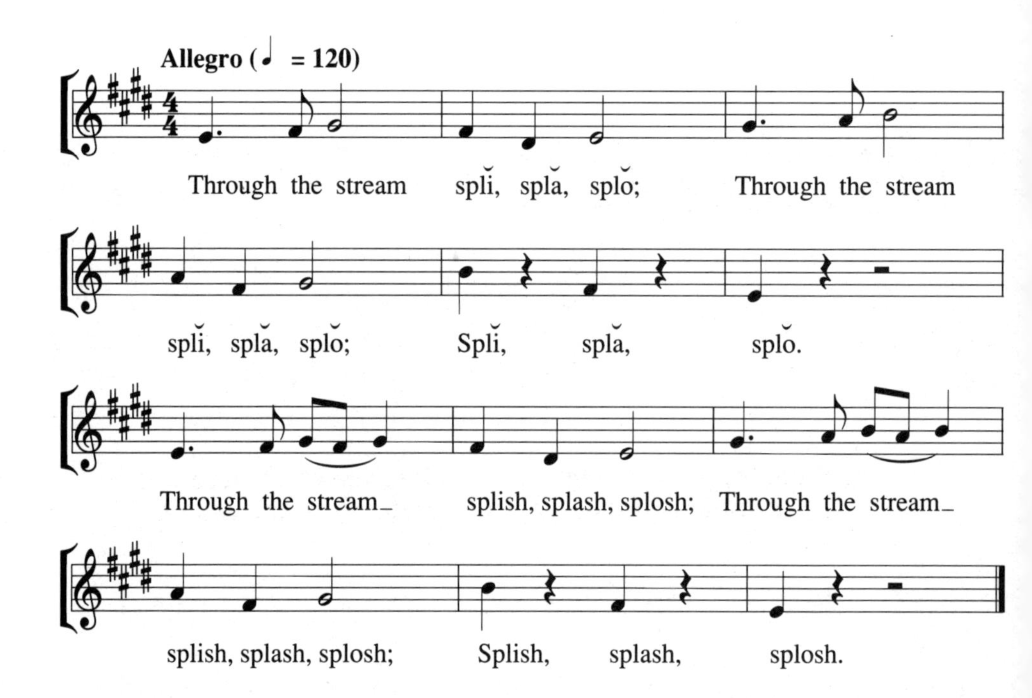
Allegro (♩ = 120)
Through the stream splĭ, splă, splŏ; Through the stream
splĭ, splă, splŏ; Splĭ, splă, splŏ.
Through the stream splish, splash, splosh; Through the stream
splish, splash, splosh; Splish, splash, splosh.

TIPS

A. Go through the triple consonants as quickly as possible. When there are three consonants right before the beat, start a bit earlier.

B. Move your lips as little as possible for clean consonants.

C. Sing the "sh" lightly on the rest:

Spli - sh, spla - sh, splo - sh,

14

tuning a rising melody

Andante (♩ = 88)
Sop.
mf unis.
Alto
Re - joice, red rose When the
Tenor mf unis.
div.
unis.
Bass
Re - joice, red rose When the

sum-mer's bloom is a sweet, sweet sight.
div.
sum-mer's bloom is a sweet, sweet, sweet sight.

TIPS

A. **Before doing a warmup with an extended range, make sure that your breathing is working well and that the middle part of your range is warmed up.**

B. **Notice how solid it feels when you sing in the center of the pitch.**

C. **Concentrate on tuning each pitch that is in the framework of the tonic chord first:**

Then it is easier to tune the other pitches in the warmup.

D. **Flip each "r" very lightly with your tongue.**

REMINDER **Practice the skills you learn in your warmup during the rest of the rehearsal as you sing your repertoire.**

15

syncopation

Quickly (♩ = 126)
unis. p – f
Parts 1, 2&3
Must the lit-tle chil - dren
suf - - fer?
Part 1
A - men, a - men,
Part 2
Part 3
Heav - en, I'm sing-in' A - men;
a - men, a - men.
Heav - en, I'm sing-in' A - men.

TIPS

A. Practice a precise syncopation by singing slowly and adding an "h" for the second note of each tie:

Must thah-hah lit-tle chil - dre-hen
sah hah fuh-huh?

REPEAT with a single vowel sound, but still feel where the second note starts. When the syncopation is accurate, smooth out the phrasing so that it will sound less mechanical.

B. Do not use excessive head movement.

C. Do not let your chin stretch forward during the *crescendo*.

D. Notice how low your jaw drops for the "ah" of "Amen." Let your jaw drop way down for the short "e" in "Amen," too.

16

consistent tone quality for small leaps

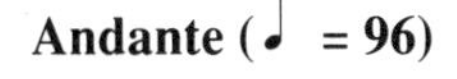
Andante (♩ = 96)

Ah,
ah,
ah,
ah,

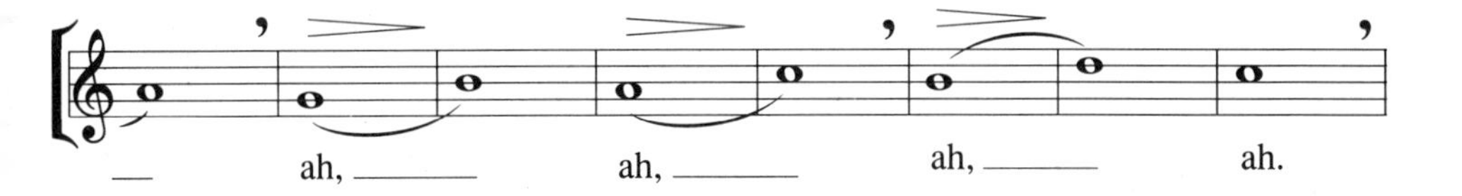
ah,
ah,
ah,
ah.

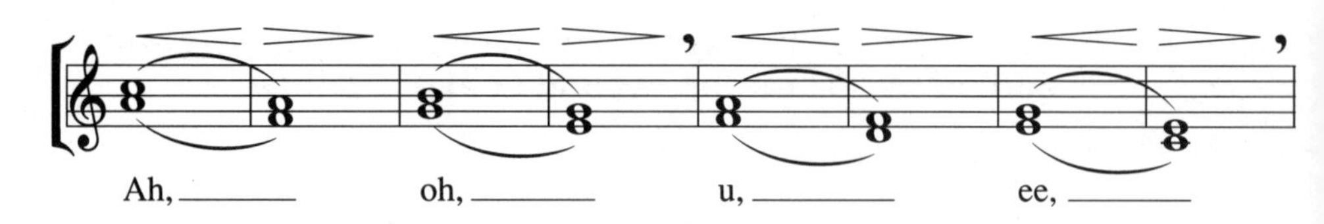
Ah,
oh,
u,
ee,

ay,
ah,
oh,
u.

TIPS

A. Match the second pitch of each pair with the quality of tone of the first pitch.

B. Let the dynamics help you even out the tone.

17

accents

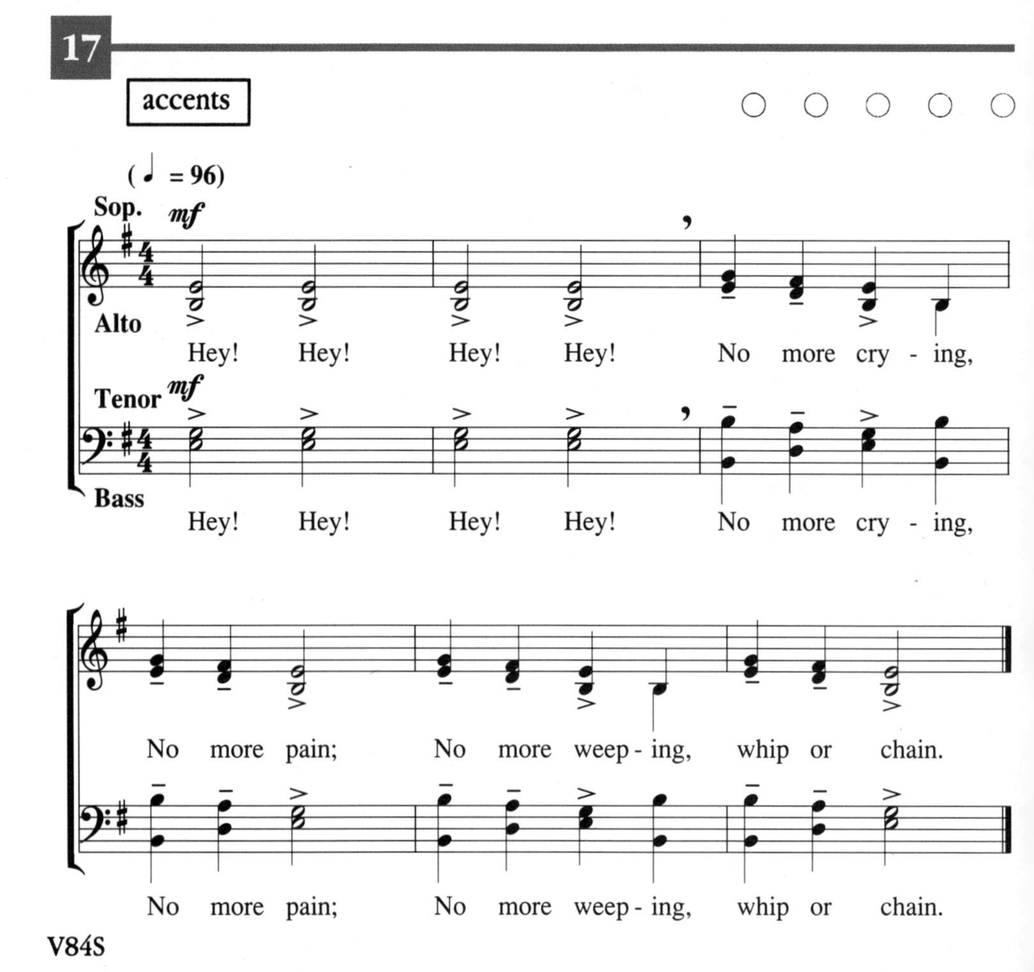
(♩ = 96)
Sop.
mf
Alto
Hey! Hey! Hey! Hey! No more cry - ing,
Tenor
mf
Bass
Hey! Hey! Hey! Hey! No more cry - ing,
No more pain; No more weep - ing, whip or chain.
No more pain; No more weep - ing, whip or chain.

TIPS

A. Keep your throat relaxed for all accents.

B. Start the > accent with a sharp jab from the tummy. Let the sound die down immediately and continue the sound at a softer level (e.g. no obvious space between notes).

C. Start the  **accent with a push from the tummy for each accent. Leave a very short space before the next note.**

18

inner rhythms

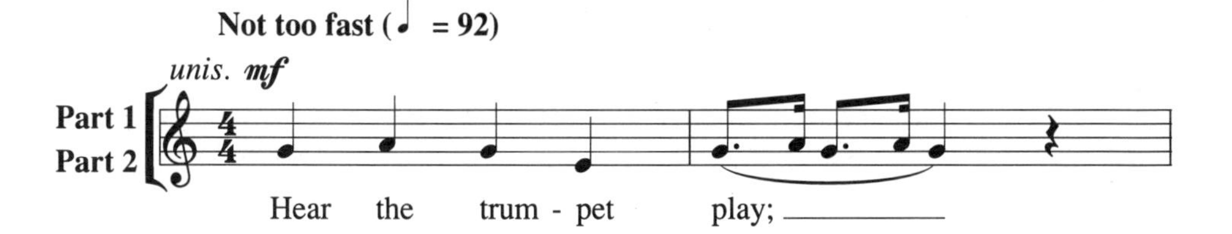
Not too fast (♩ = 92)
unis. mf
Part 1
Part 2
Hear the trum - pet play;

div.
Hear the trum-pet play; hear the trum-pet play.

TIPS

A. Imagine you can hear the sixteenth note pulses of an accompanying orchestra. These are the *inner rhythms* which give life to the music.

B. Each sixteenth note should be exactly in time:

19

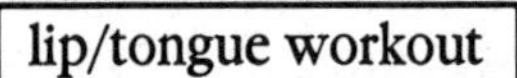

lip/tongue workout

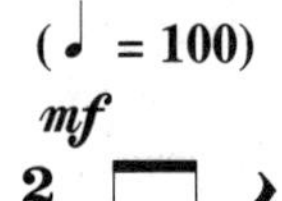
(♩ = 100)
mf
2
4
V v

v v

b b

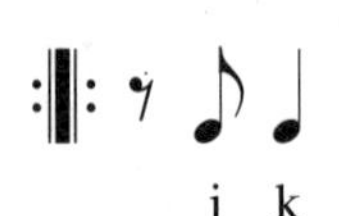
j k

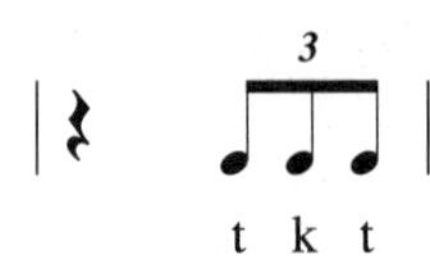
3
t k t

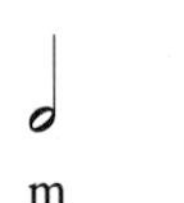
m

p t p t
p t

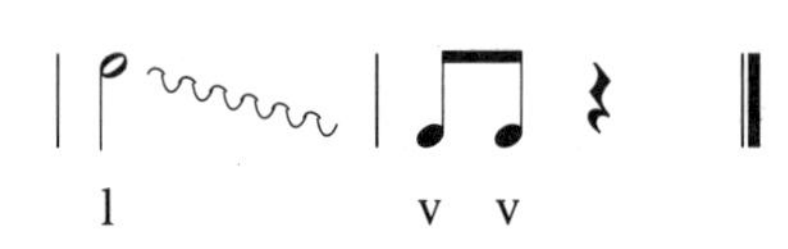
l
v v

TIPS

A. Articulate each consonant clearly.

B. The character of the consonants can be changed for the mood (or language) of the music:

firm for more energy (German) or relaxed for a gentler quality (Spanish)

When the consonants are relaxed, you still go through the consonants quickly but you relax the muscles of the tongue and lips.

20

quality for high pitches

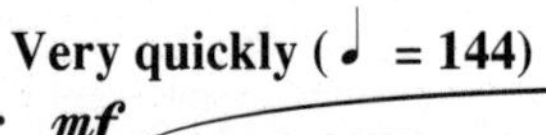
Very quickly (♩ = 144)

Sop.
mf
3
4
Alto 1. Ee,
2. U,
Tenor
3
4
Bass

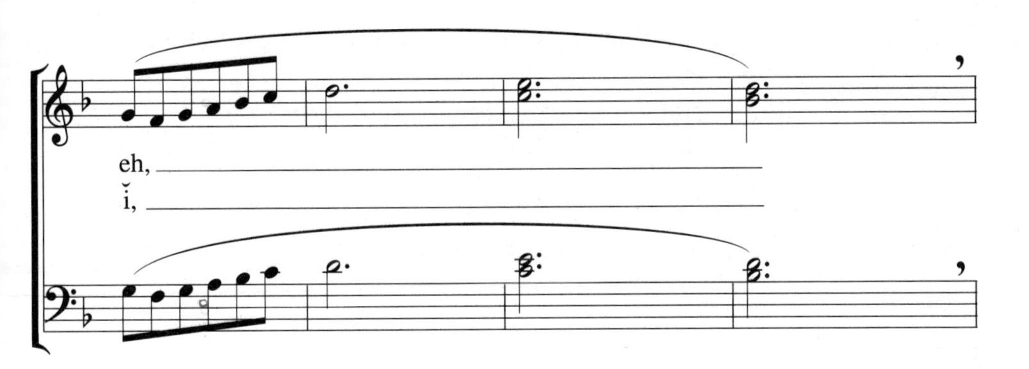
eh,
ĭ,

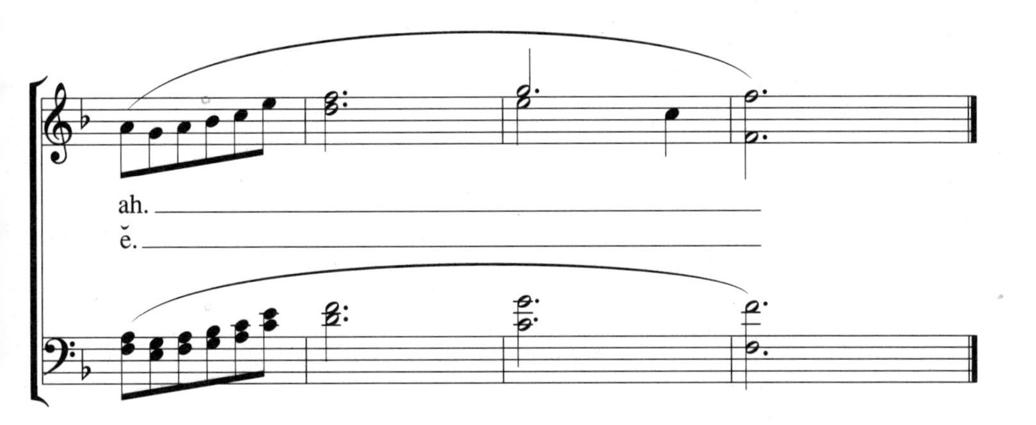
ah.
ĕ.

TIPS

A. On the long high notes, imagine each tone is ringing like a huge, vibrant bell:

Sopranos: in a circle connecting your upper teeth to your forehead	**Altos:** throughout your head and upper chest
Tenors: in a circle that covers your entire head	**Basses:** in your teeth, the roof of your mouth and your chest, but not in the back of your throat

TIPS
(cont.)

B. For "ee" and "ay," keep your jaw down and relax your throat.

C. When your voice sounds good, imagine you are taking a "snapshot" of the sound. Remember that snapshot later when you try to reproduce the same quality of sound.

D. For short vowels, keep the sound as warm and full as possible.

21
pp; tuning with dissonance
Slowly (♩ = 72)
pp
What joy! What joy! What joy! A - gain we say: re - joice.
pp

TIPS

A. **** Multiple Choice ****

pp **means:**

a) Soggy;
b) Muted;
c) You should have eaten a better breakfast;
d) Low on volume but high on energy.

B. For *pp*, imagine that you are invisible. Everyone can hear you clearly but they cannot see you.

C. For slow music, feed the vowels but put the consonants on a diet.

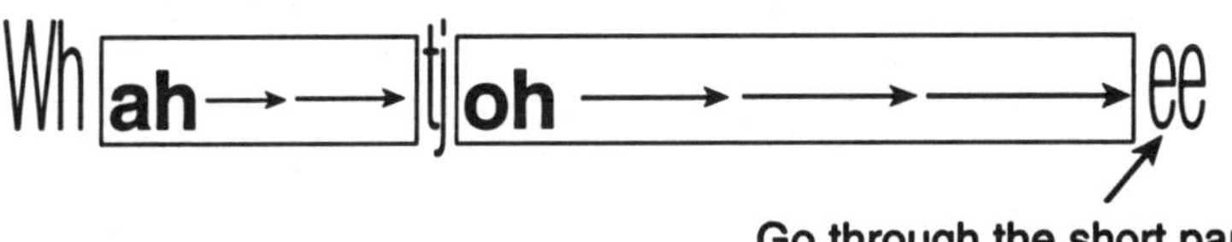
Wh
ah
tj
oh
ee

Go through the short part of the diphthong quickly.

REMINDER **Drink plenty of water every day.**

SINGERS IN POSITION

Pretend you are balancing a basket on your head.

22

tuning perfect fifths

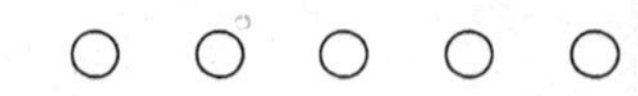

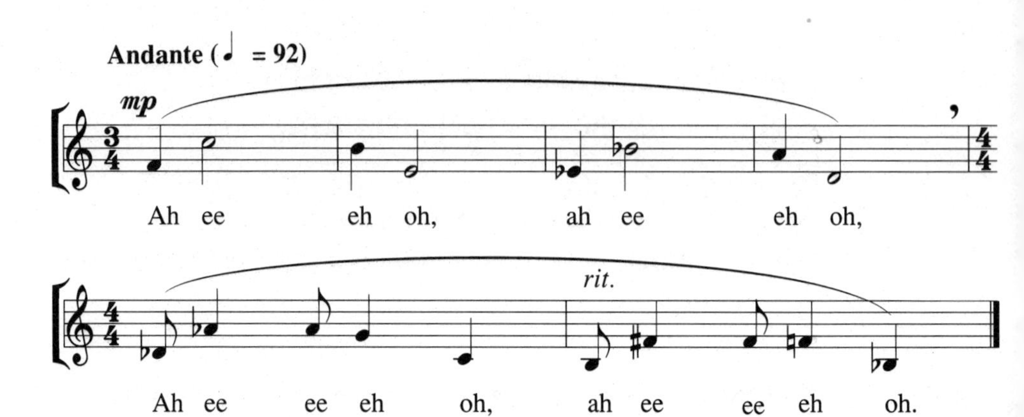
Andante (♩ = 92)
mp
Ah ee eh oh, ah ee eh oh,
rit.
Ah ee ee eh oh, ah ee ee eh oh.

TIPS	
	A. Sing slowly. Do not glide between pitches.
	B. For better tuning, focus the low pitches; relax the high pitches.

23

"ow"

ow = a diphthong made from two sounds:

ah + u

(u = sounds like the "oo" in "moon")

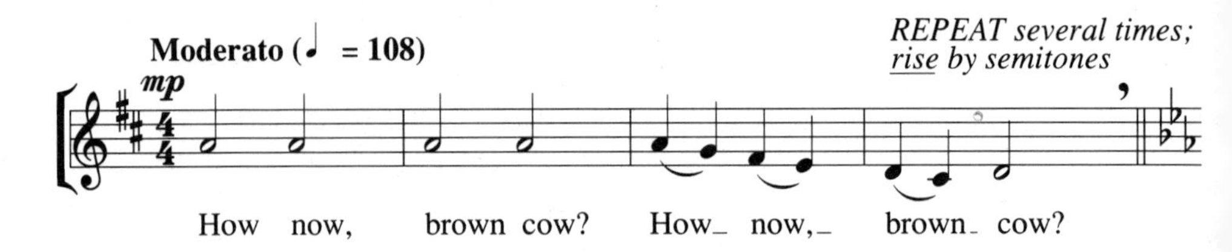
Moderato (♩ = 108)
REPEAT several times; rise by semitones
mp
How now, brown cow? How_ now,_ brown_ cow?

TIP **Do not go to the second vowel too soon during the slurred notes.**

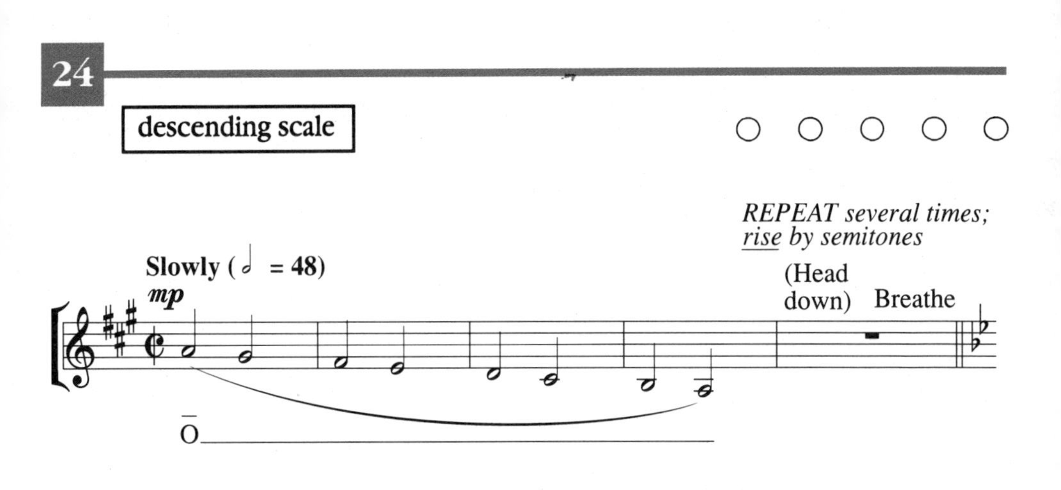
24
descending scale
REPEAT several times; rise by semitones
Slowly (𝅗𝅥 = 48)
mp
(Head down)
Breathe
Ō

TIPS

A. Lean your head forward and down before the beginning of each scale. Slowly straighten as the pitch descends.

B. Keep the lower pitches light. Feel the pitches float gently out as your head rises.

REMINDER **Practice the skills you learn in your warmup during the rest of the rehearsal as you sing your repertoire.**

25

vowels modified by final "l"

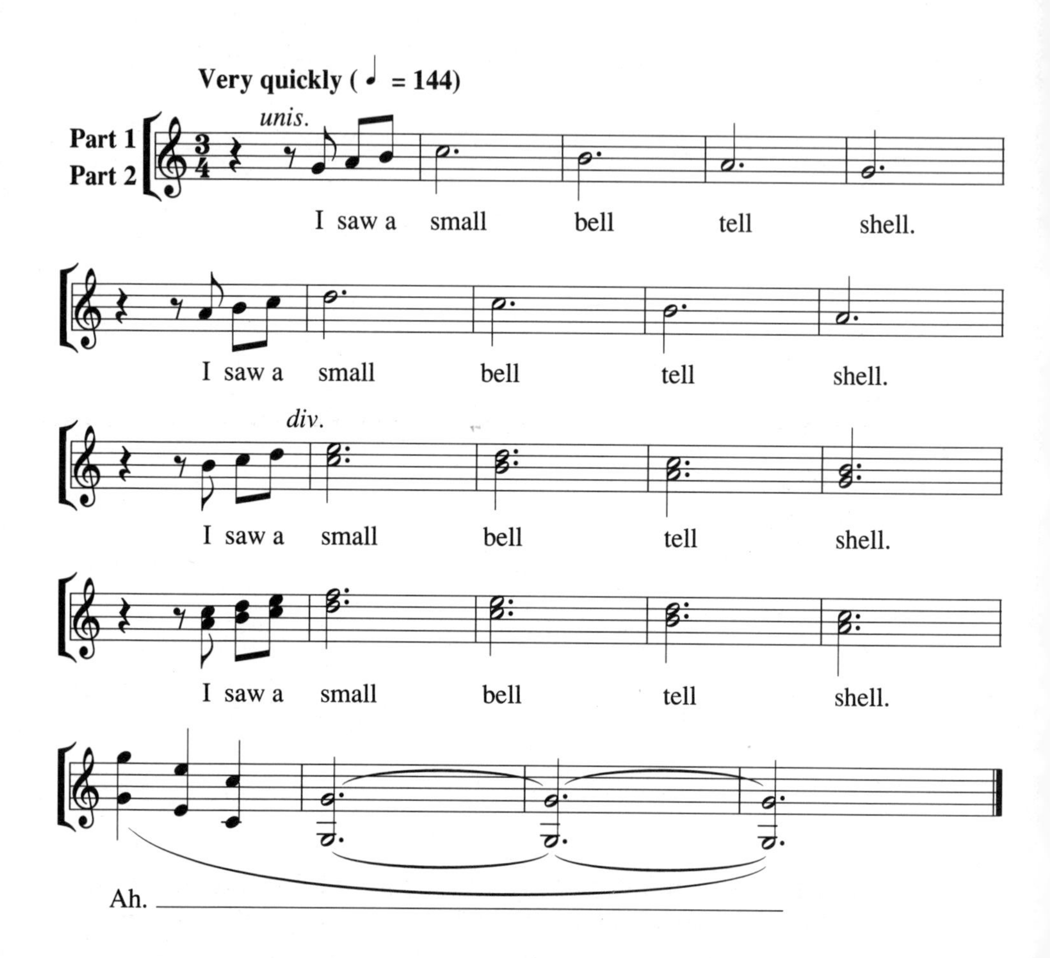

Very quickly (♩ = 144)
Part 1
Part 2
unis.
I saw a small bell tell shell.
I saw a small bell tell shell.
div.
I saw a small bell tell shell.
I saw a small bell tell shell.
Ah.

TIPS

A. Do not sing each "l" until the last possible moment.

B. If your tongue starts gradually rising for the "l" too early, you will:

- **Lose the purity of the vowel that comes before "l";**
- **Go sharp.**

26

quick "ng" warmup

○ ○ ○ ○ ○

Slowly (♩ = 63)
mf
1. Ding dong ding dong ding dong ding dong; Ding dong ding dong
2. King kong king kong king kong king kong; King kong king kong
3. Ping pong ping pong ping pong ping pong; Ping pong ping pong

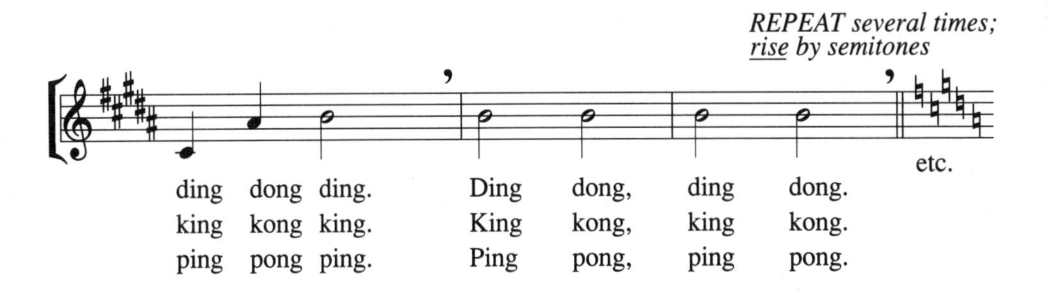
REPEAT several times; rise by semitones
ding dong ding. Ding dong, ding dong.
king kong king. King kong, king kong.
ping pong ping. Ping pong, ping pong.
etc.

TIPS

A. For a quick warmup, go to the "ng" quickly right after the vowel. Feel the outline of your head vibrate with each "ng":

In concert music, you would not go quickly to the "ng" except for a sound effect.

B. Let each "d" throw the voice placement forward.

C. Feel the resonance as one continuous flow rather than note by note.

D. Breathe quickly and deeply between phrases.

cat glide

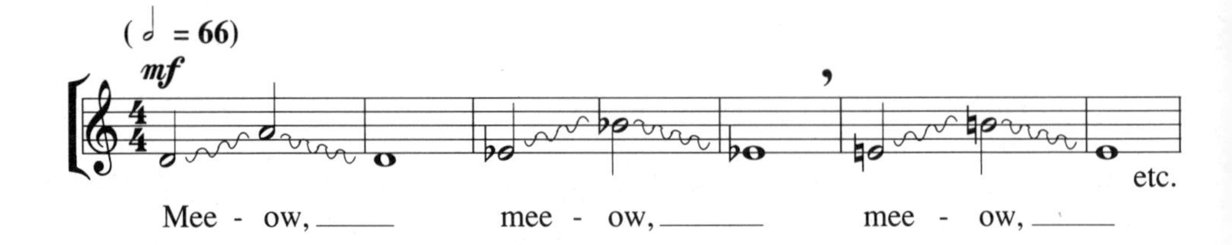
(𝅗𝅥 = 66)
mf
etc.
Mee - ow,
mee - ow,
mee - ow,

TIPS

A. Sing a variety of cat sounds. The quality of tone may not sound very musical, but it will help to warm up the middle and upper parts of the range.

B. Feel as if the roof of your mouth is vibrating.

C. Feel as if your eye sockets are vibrating.

D. Feel as if the top of your head is vibrating.

"or"

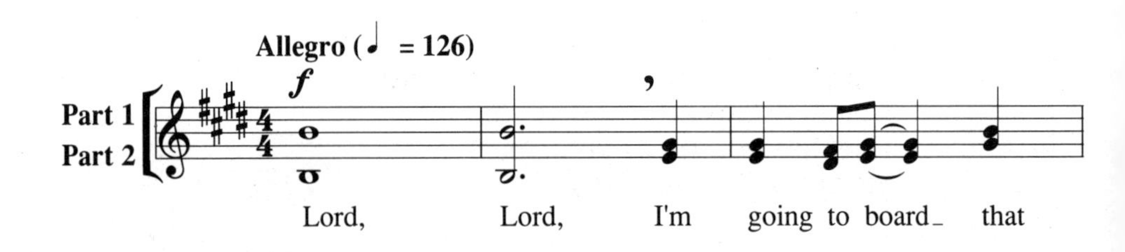
Allegro (♩ = 126)
f
Part 1
Part 2
Lord,
Lord,
I'm
going to board
that

morn - ing train,
oo
oo.
I'm

going to board_ that morn - ing train, _ oo ____ oo. ____

____ I'm going to board_ that morn- ing train, _ oo ____

____ oo. ____

TIPS

To avoid stressing the ugly "r":

A. Place the tip of your tongue where your lower teeth meet the gums and flatten the front of your tongue.

B. Keep your jaw down.

C. Cross out the "r" in concert repertoire: Lord.

REMINDER **Start each day with a morning hum.**

29

improving low notes

Slowly (♩ = 84)
mf
Spin spin spin spin wee wee wee.

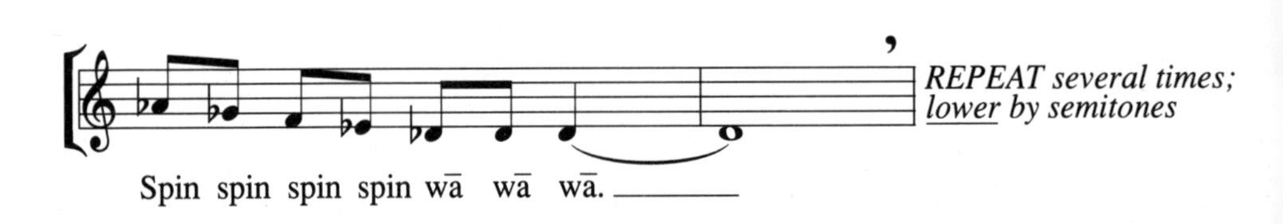
Spin spin spin spin wā wā wā.
REPEAT several times;
lower by semitones

For the repeats use "wah" "woh" "bee" "bā" "bah" "boh" after each "Spin spin spin spin."

REMINDER **Whenever your tone sounds exceptionally good, take a "snapshot" of the sound.**

TIPS

A. Go to the "n" quickly for each "spin."

B. Let the resonance of the "n" go forward into the "wee wee wee."

C. If your voice only produces a very weak sound on the lower pitches, sing lightly and do not push. The resonance will gradually improve.

D. For low pitches, feel a warm glow of resonance:

Sopranos:

In a circle around your face. Make sure the circle includes your chin.

Altos:

In a ball shape inside your mouth. Include your throat.

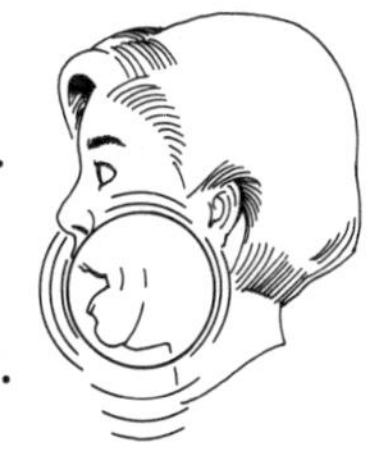

Tenors:

From your upper chest to your forehead.

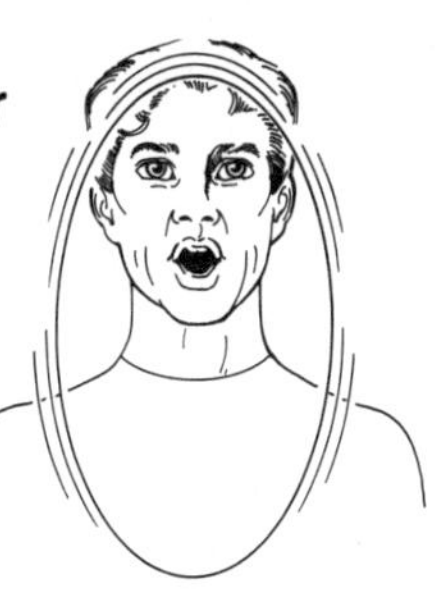

Basses:

In an oval from your upper teeth to your waist.

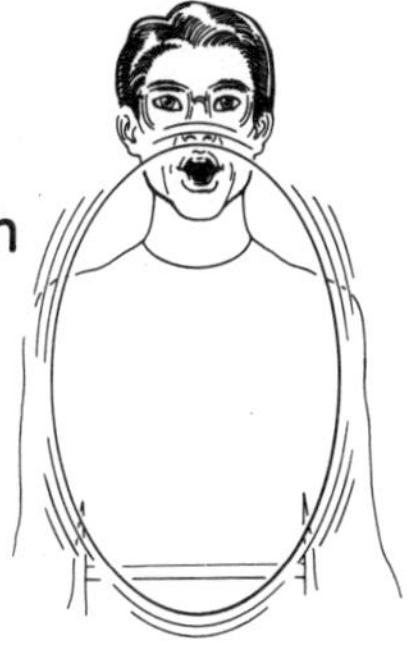

E. Focus the tone on the low pitches.

30

long melisma

Andante (♩ = 84 - 100)
G. F. Handel
mp
For un - to us a child is born

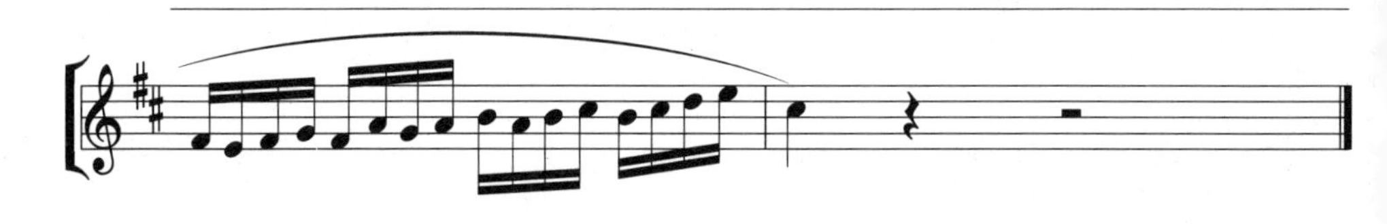

TIPS

A. In concert music, it may help to write the vowel at the beginning of each bar as a reminder:

oh
oh

B. In Baroque counterpoint, the fabric of the music seems to "breathe" in and out as the excitement of the different vocal lines rise to climax and then ease off. If you sing with the momentum of each phrase and then relax, the melismas:

- **Sound more musical;**
- **Are easier to sing.**

Listen to the natural flow of the group singing to determine where the climaxes come.

C. Sing this warmup to "dee," "dī" or "du." Each vowel needs to be worked out separately.

31

stagger breathing

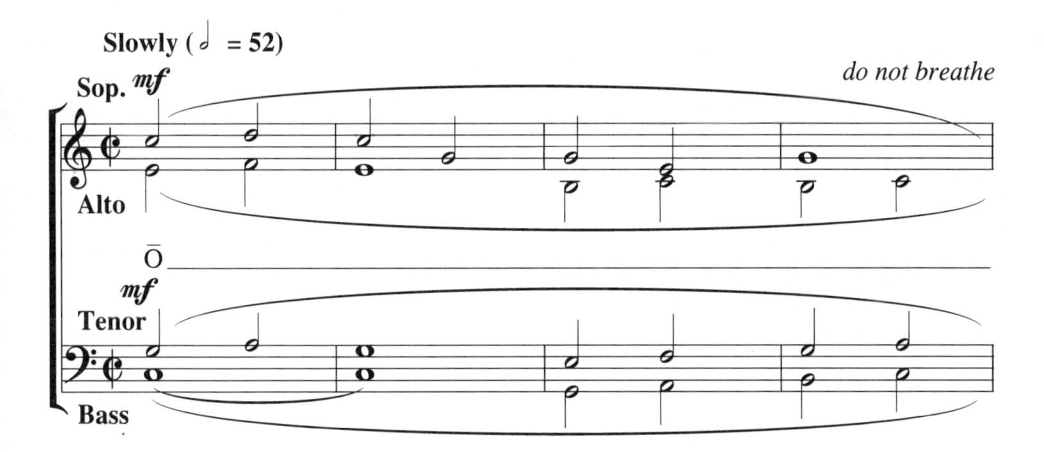
Slowly (𝅗𝅥 = 52)
do not breathe
Sop. mf
Alto
Ō
mf
Tenor
Bass

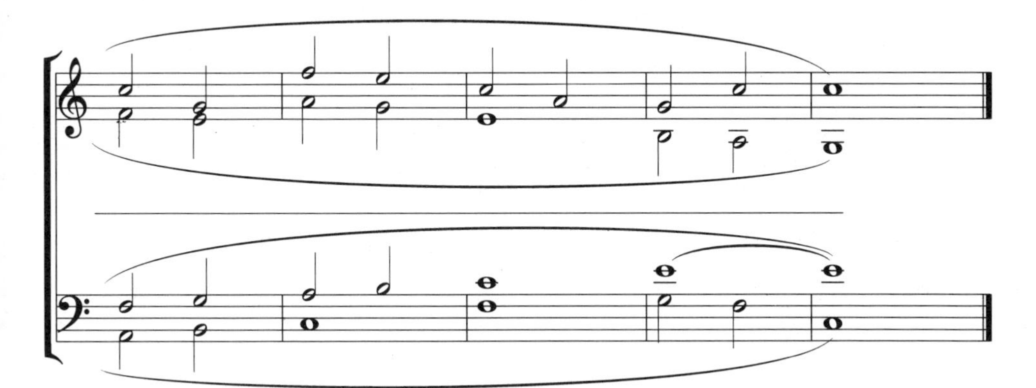

TIPS

A. For the long phrases, stagger your breath with the singers around you (e.g. breathe at a different time than your neighbor).

B. To hide your breathing spot:

1) Before each staggered breath, do a *dim.*

2) Breathe quietly!

3) Re-enter quietly and then *crescendo* up to the correct dynamic level.

C. Do not breathe between phrases; choose a less obvious place to breathe.

D. Check the tuning during the *dim.* and *cresc.* of the staggered breath.

32

octave leaps

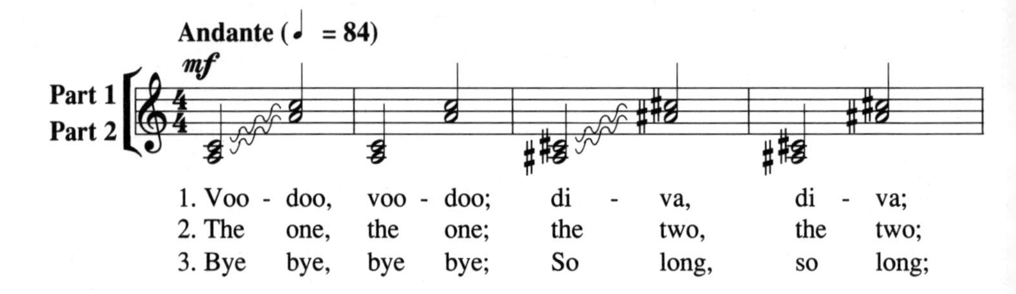
Andante (♩ = 84)
mf
Part 1
Part 2
1. Voo - doo, voo - doo; di - va, di - va;
2. The one, the one; the two, the two;
3. Bye bye, bye bye; So long, so long;

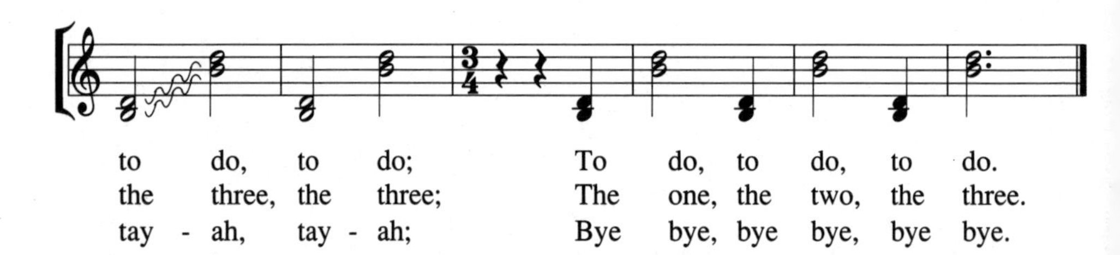
to do, to do; To do, to do, to do.
the three, the three; The one, the two, the three.
tay - ah, tay - ah; Bye bye, bye bye, bye bye.

TIPS

A. For a clean leap on a single vowel sound:

1) *Diminuendo* on the lower pitch.
2) Suddenly drop the jaw and increase the air pressure for the higher pitch.

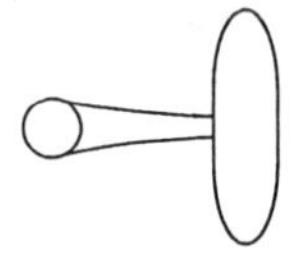

Voo - doo

There should be no space between the two pitches.

B. Sing the consonant at the same pitch as the higher note to help you with the leap:

voo-<u>d</u>oo

C. For a clean leap on a diphthong ("bye"):

1) *Crescendo* on the first part of the diphthong ("bah").
2) Sing the second part of the diphthong ("ee") very quickly and lightly at the last possible moment.
3) Suddenly drop the jaw and increase the air pressure for the higher pitch.

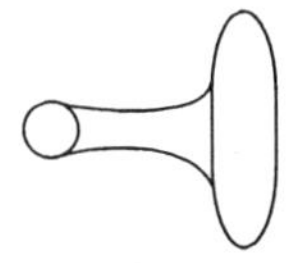

Bah - eebye

D. Do <u>not</u>:

- Let the second part of the diphthong ("ee") glide up;
- Add a "y" sound: *tehee-yah.*

E. When the lungs and vocal folds become coated with smoke, the singer cannot use the natural beauty or the full power of their voice. Even light smokers are handicapped.

33

articulation

Not too quickly (𝅗𝅥 = 66)

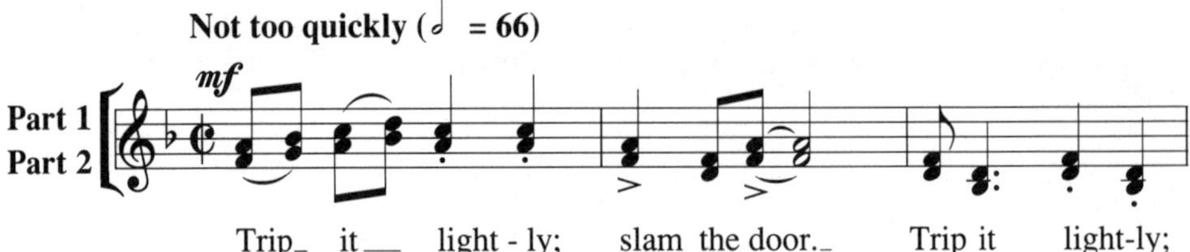
Part 1
Part 2
mf

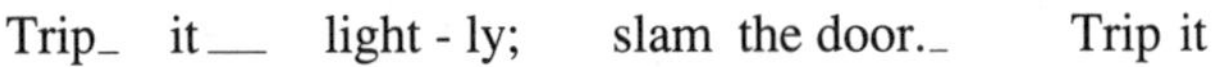
Trip_ it__ light - ly; slam the door._ Trip it light-ly;

back for more. Trip_ it, trip_ it slam the door.

TIPS

A. Be alert. Let your eyes check ahead for special markings.

B. For better precision, let your eyes flick up to the downbeat of the conductor at the first note of each bar.

C. If there are no accents or staccato markings, sing *legato*.

34

matching the entry with the piano

○ ○ ○ ○ ○

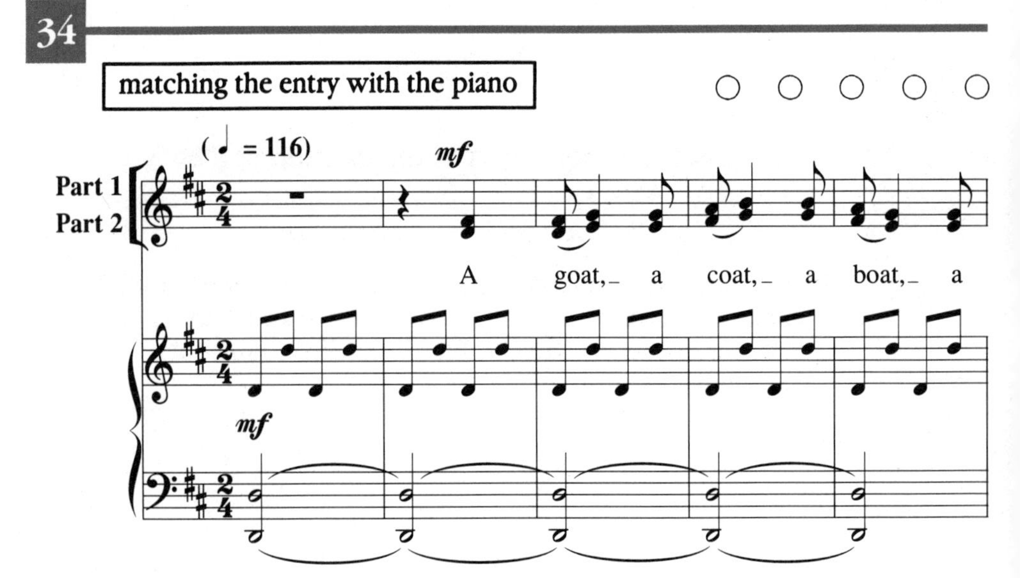
(♩ = 116)
mf
Part 1
Part 2
A goat,_ a coat,_ a boat,_ a
mf

moat.
A

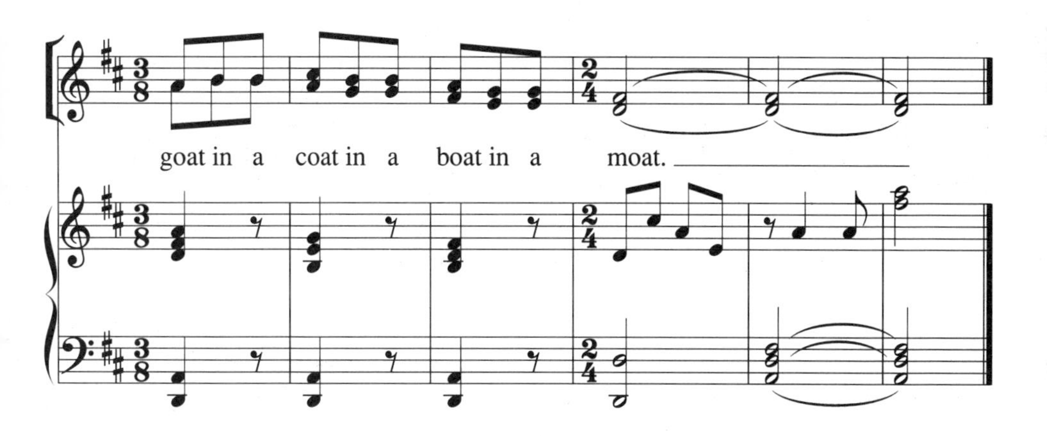
goat in a coat in a boat in a moat.

TIPS

A. Music is a total art-form; the relationship of the piano and voice is an important part of the overall effect. Let the vocal part continue naturally on from the piano part.

B. In concert music, know exactly when your entry comes. Mark your score.

C. Remember to start your breath early in rhythm.

D. Feel as if you are a part of the music the piano is playing.

35

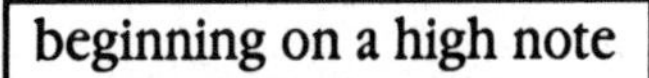
beginning on a high note

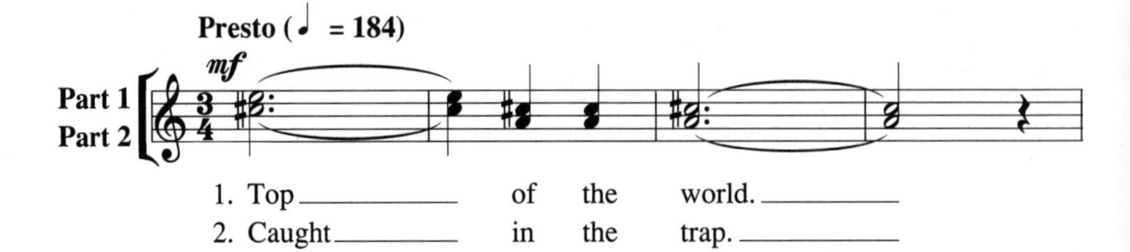
Presto (♩ = 184)
mf
Part 1
Part 2
1. Top of the world.
2. Caught in the trap.

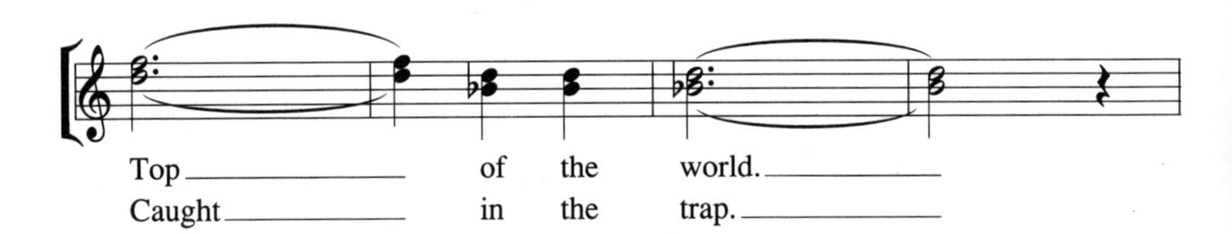
Top of the world.
Caught in the trap.

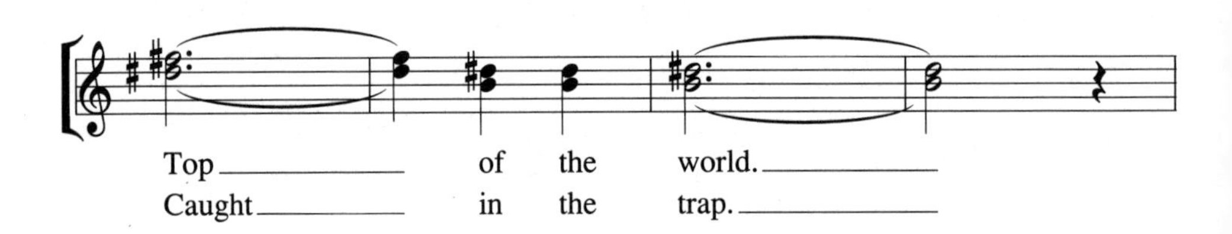
Top of the world.
Caught in the trap.

Top of the world.
Caught in the trap.

TIPS

- **A. Let your jaw drop for the vowel.**
- **B. Feel the high note start with a "ping" in the top of your forehead.**
- **C. Relax the throat during each quick breath.**
- **D. Start the initial consonants at the same pitch as the vowel or the sound may swoop up to the vowel.**
- **E. Do not practice high pitches for too long at a time.**

36

whole tones

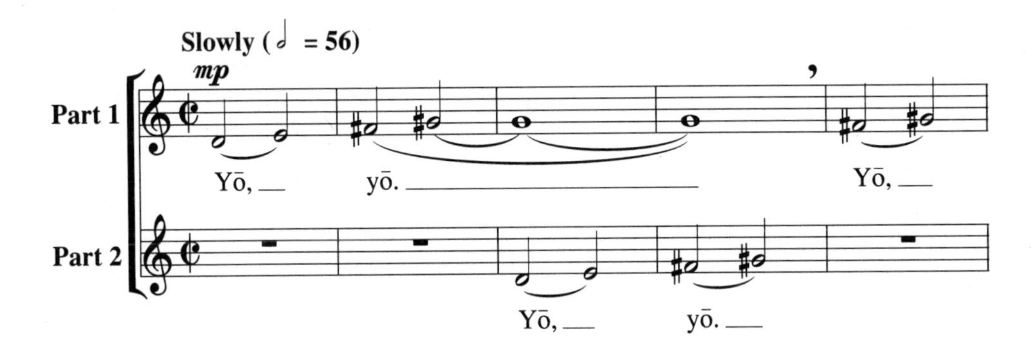
Slowly (𝅗𝅥 = 56)
mp
Part 1
Part 2
Yō, yō. Yō,
Yō, yō.

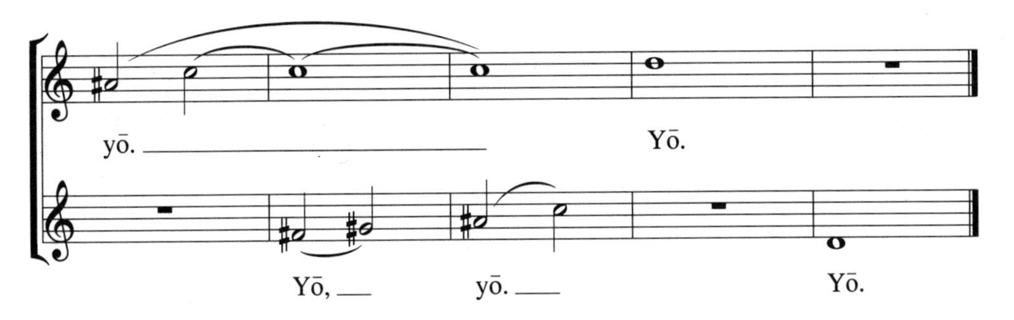
yō. Yō.
Yō, yō. Yō.

TIPS

A. There is no tonal center in a whole tone scale — no sense of heading toward one pitch which is stronger than the others. The music has an unusual "floating" sensation.

B. Go quickly through the "y": not "eeyō."

37

fast and loud lyrics

Quickly (♩. = 88)
f
Yes - ter - day was a flur - ry of mo - tion; soon it will be to -

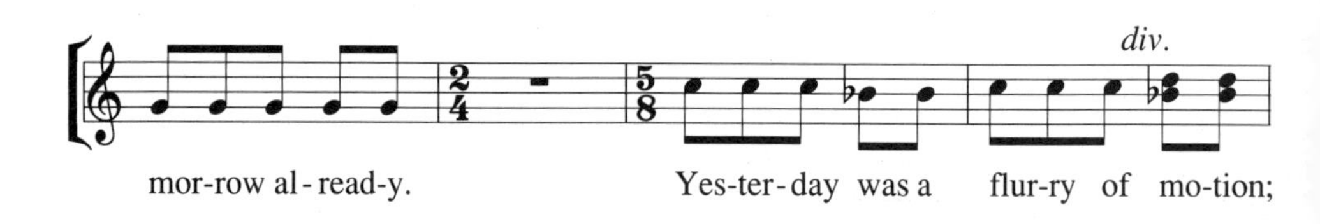
div.
mor-row al - read-y. Yes-ter-day was a flur-ry of mo-tion;

unis.
soon it will be to - mor-row al-read-y. Yes-ter-day was a

flur - ry of mo - tion; soon it will be to - mor-row al - read-y.

TIPS

A. Use a smaller focus of sound for a fast *forte* passage but use as much resonance as possible.

B. Focus all your consonants on one thing at the back of the hall.

C. You can create the illusion of more volume if the consonants are clear and focused. Do not over-articulate and let the consonants spit out from the sides of your mouth.

THIRD YEAR PROGRESS CHART

CIRCLE the appropriate number:

1 - understands the skill
2 - can do the skill
3 - some improvement shown
4 - good progress
5 - excellent progress
6 - remembers consistently

Singers in Position - ready for anything	1 2 3 4 5 6
1a. gentle warmup - hum; five vowels	1 2 3 4 5 6
1b. different phrase lengths	1 2 3 4 5 6
1c. slurs	1 2 3 4 5 6
1d. resonance on low pitches	1 2 3 4 5 6
1e. $\genfrac{}{}{0pt}{}{5}{8}$ $\genfrac{}{}{0pt}{}{7}{8}$	1 2 3 4 5 6
Breathing - clothing not restrictive	1 2 3 4 5 6
- lengthen spine	1 2 3 4 5 6
- breathe early in rhythm	1 2 3 4 5 6
- mark breathing places	1 2 3 4 5 6
2. ī	1 2 3 4 5 6
3. tuning semitones	1 2 3 4 5 6
4. sixteenth notes	1 2 3 4 5 6
Singers in Position - sit ready to stand	1 2 3 4 5 6
5. glides for consistent tone	1 2 3 4 5 6
Quick check: Drinking water?	1 2 3 4 5 6
6. continuing the idea through the rests	1 2 3 4 5 6
7. staccato	1 2 3 4 5 6
8. tuning harmonically	1 2 3 4 5 6
Singers in Position - light folders	1 2 3 4 5 6
- elbows forward	1 2 3 4 5 6
9. resonance	1 2 3 4 5 6
10. internal "r"	1 2 3 4 5 6
11. short "e i u"	1 2 3 4 5 6
12. *forte* and *piano* - clarity	1 2 3 4 5 6
- no change in tuning or tempo with dynamic change	1 2 3 4 5 6
Quick check: Open throat?	1 2 3 4 5 6
13. thr str spl	1 2 3 4 5 6
14. tuning a rising melody	1 2 3 4 5 6

Quick check: Concentrating on warmups	1 2 3 4 5 6
15. syncopation	1 2 3 4 5 6
16. consistent tone quality for small leaps	1 2 3 4 5 6
17. accents	1 2 3 4 5 6
18. inner rhythms	1 2 3 4 5 6
Quick check: Posture?	1 2 3 4 5 6
19. lip/tongue workout	1 2 3 4 5 6
20. quality for high pitches	1 2 3 4 5 6
21. *pp*	1 2 3 4 5 6
tuning with dissonance	1 2 3 4 5 6
quick consonants for slow music	1 2 3 4 5 6
Singers in Position - basket on your head	1 2 3 4 5 6
22. tuning perfect fifths	1 2 3 4 5 6
23. ow	1 2 3 4 5 6
24. descending scale	1 2 3 4 5 6
25. vowels modified by final "l"	1 2 3 4 5 6
Quick check: Forward tone?	1 2 3 4 5 6
26. quick "ng" warmup	1 2 3 4 5 6
27. cat glide	1 2 3 4 5 6
28. "or"	1 2 3 4 5 6
29. improving low notes	1 2 3 4 5 6
30. long melisma	1 2 3 4 5 6
- mark vowel in score	1 2 3 4 5 6
- climaxes	1 2 3 4 5 6
Quick check: Breathing?	1 2 3 4 5 6
31. stagger breathing	1 2 3 4 5 6
32. octave leaps - vowel	1 2 3 4 5 6
- diphthong	1 2 3 4 5 6
33. articulation	1 2 3 4 5 6
34. matching the entry with the piano	1 2 3 4 5 6
- mark your entry	1 2 3 4 5 6
35. beginning on a high note	1 2 3 4 5 6
36. whole tones	1 2 3 4 5 6
37. fast and loud lyrics	1 2 3 4 5 6

◆◆ CONGRATULATIONS! ◆◆

Fourth Year

Each human voice has as many timbres as the elements of the earth: Fire, Water, Metal, Earth, Wood.

SINGERS IN POSITION

Take pride in your singing. Stand like a VIP:

- Confident;
- Prepared to use your best quality voice;
- Ready for new opportunities for improvement.

Imagine that the top of your head is suspended from a thread:

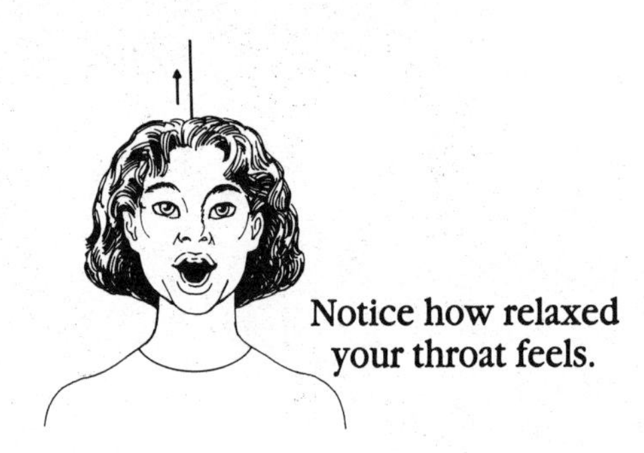
Notice how relaxed
your throat feels.

38

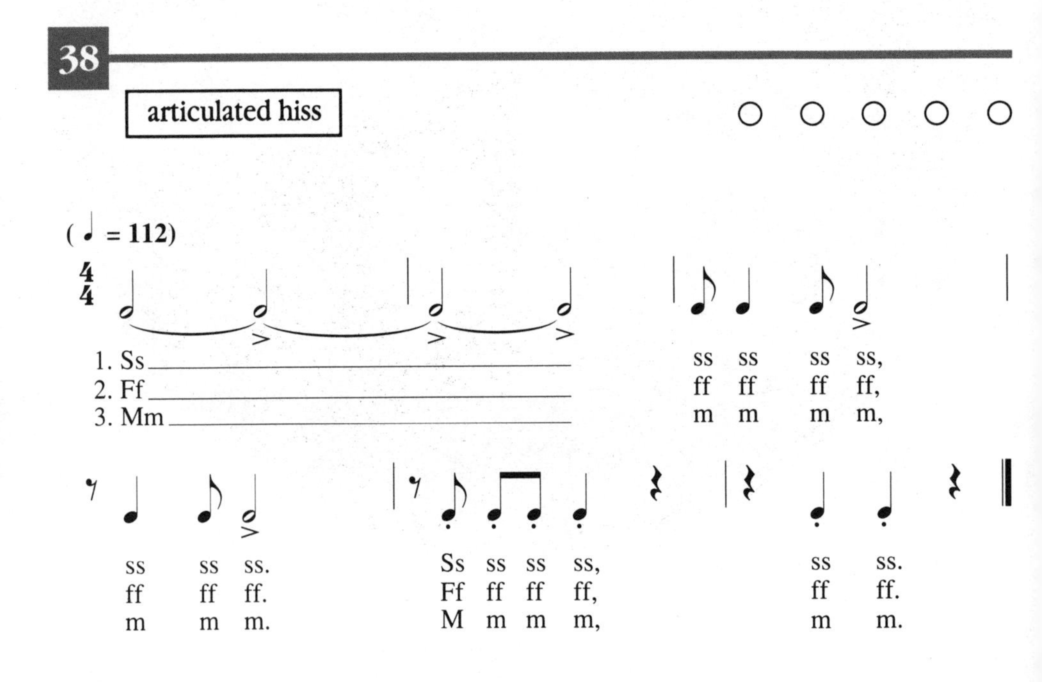
articulated hiss
(♩ = 112)
4/4
1. Ss
2. Ff
3. Mm
ss ss ss ss,
ff ff ff ff,
m m m m,
ss ss ss.
ff ff ff.
m m m.
Ss ss ss ss,
Ff ff ff ff,
M m m m,
ss ss.
ff ff.
m m.

TIP **Use one hiss for the first two bars. During that hiss, make the accents with a quick, sharp bounce from the tummy.**

REMINDER **Drink plenty of water each day. Start each day with a morning hum.**

39

even resonance

Quickly (♩ = 126)
REPEAT several times; rise by semitones
mf
Mm,
U.

TIPS

A. The color or timbre of your voice may change slightly (and delightfully) in different parts of your range but <u>the basic foundation of the tone quality should remain the same</u>. It should not sound as if you are "shifting gears" as you move from low to high. This would destroy the continuity of the melodic line.

B. Make the lower pitches in each phrase brighter to match the higher pitches better.

C. Make the higher pitches fuller and richer like the lower pitches.

D. As you move into the higher pitches, do not let the volume suddenly increase.

E. It is easier to match the resonance throughout the range when you sing with an open throat.

40

rubato

Quickly (♩ = 126)
REPEAT several times; rise by semitones
mf
U.

TIPS

A. Rubato:

move more quickly; relax the tempo

Use rubato to create a slight sense of temporary excitement followed by relaxation:

B. Be kind to your ears; avoid noise pollution. Your hearing can be permanently damaged by:

- **very loud noises;**
- **moderately loud, continuous noises. The effect of the noise is multiplied by the length of time it continues.**

41

range extension down

(♩ = 84)
mf
REPEAT several times;
lower by semitones
Breathe, 2
Zee-ah zee-ah zee-ah zee-ah zee-ah zee-ah zay.

TIPS

A. Use as much resonance as possible for the lower pitches.

B. Do not push the *crescendo*. Use the tummy to make the sound swell more naturally.

C. Focus the pitch for the lower notes.

D. Sing with your eyes (as well as your mouth) for a brighter, more forward tone.

REMINDER

To hear your own voice better when singing alone, sing into a corner.

42

cresc. dim.

Quickly (♩ = 126)
Sop.
Alto
1. 1 2 3 4 5 6 7 8 9 10 11 12.
2. Nah nee nee, nah nee nee, nah nee nee, nah nee nee.
Tenor
Bass

1 2 3 4 5 6 7 8 9 10 e-lev'n 12.
Nah nee nee, nah nee nee, nah nee nee, nah nee nee nee.

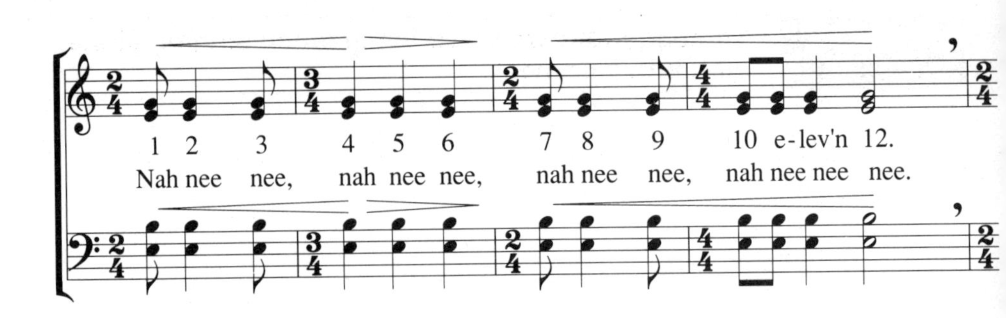
1 2 3 4 5 6 7 8 9 10 e-lev'n 12.
Nah nee nee, nah nee nee, nah nee nee, nah nee nee nee.

1 2 3 4 5 6 7 8 9 10 e-lev'n 12.
Nah nee nee, nah nee nee, nah nee nee, nah nee nee nee.

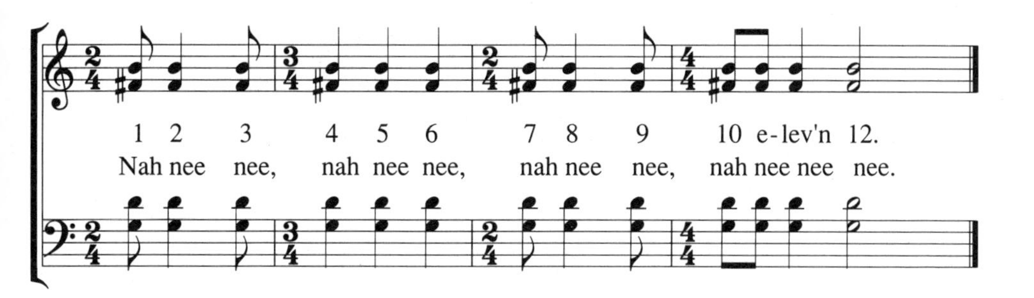
1 2 3 4 5 6 7 8 9 10 e-lev'n 12.
Nah nee nee, nah nee nee, nah nee nee, nah nee nee nee.

TIPS

A. Try singing the *cresc.* and *dim.* in different ways:

1) Start cool, get hot, then cool off again;

2) Gradually increase/slowly decrease the urgency;

3) Gradually more fun/slowly leave the party.

B. Do not distort the pitch or the color of the music during the *cresc.* or *dim.*

C. Each vowel has its own distinct sound, but one vowel should not be very bright compared to another vowel at the same pitch.

43
long *legato* phrasing
(𝅗𝅥 = 80)
Part 1
Part 2
Part 3
mf
By lie, by lie, by
Bet let, bit lit; bet let,
By lie, by lie, by by
lie. Pay kay, pay kay, pay kay,
bit lit. Pat cat, putt cut; pat cat,
lie. Pay kay, pay kay, pay kay,
pay kay.
putt cut; pat cat, putt.
pay kay, pay pay, kay.

TIPS

A. Notice how the contrary motion in Parts 1 and 3 balances one part with the other. Fit the tuning of the two parts together.

B. Use the framework pitches of the tonic chord (E and B) to stabilize the tuning.

C. Notice how the contrasting rhythms in Parts 1 and 3, and Part 2 balance each other. Fit the main beats exactly together with the conductor.

D. Sing the last two bars. Then sing the last three bars. Keep adding more bars so that the last bar always has lots of air.

44

final consonant/initial consonant

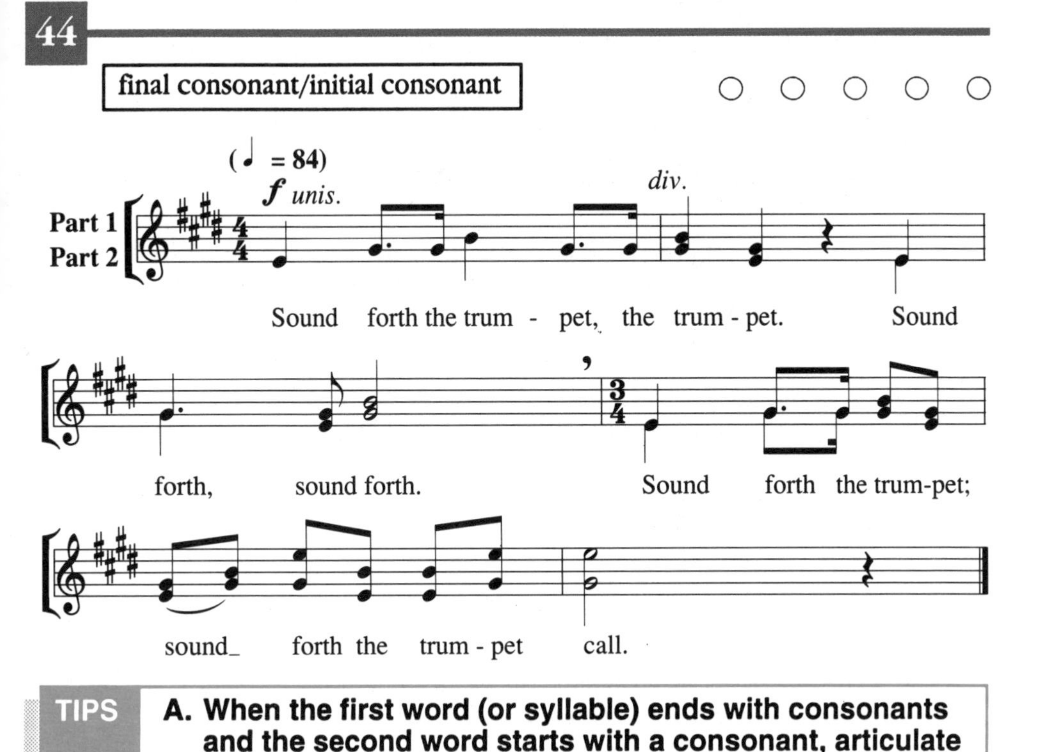
(♩ = 84)
f unis.
div.
Part 1
Part 2
Sound forth the trum - pet, the trum - pet. Sound
forth, sound forth. Sound forth the trum-pet;
sound_ forth the trum - pet call.

TIPS

A. When the first word (or syllable) ends with consonants and the second word starts with a consonant, articulate all consonants quickly and clearly:

Sou _____ ndfo _____ rth

B. Imagine your voice is like a trumpet projecting the sound forward.

PACING YOUR VOICE

When your voice is prone to becoming tired or the rehearsal is going to be very strenuous:

A. Start your own gentle warmup before the official rehearsal warmup.

B. Sip water during the rehearsal.

C. Always keep your voice relaxed and forward. Be particularly aware of this in high stress music:

- Pitched high or low for a long time;
- Same dynamic level for a long time;
- Continuous staccato or accents.

D. When singing a lot of high-pitched music:

- Remember that high pitches tend to stand out naturally and do not need as much volume. Save your voice.
- Whenever you do have a chance to sing a few lower pitches, sing right into the center of those pitches with a relaxed, resonant sound so that the mouth has a chance to completely change formation from the higher pitches ("ah, relief!").

For music that is low-pitched, concentrate on the change of formation for the few higher pitches.

E. Do not sing *f* or *ff* for too long a time without a change in the dynamics. Build up your stamina for loud notes gradually.

F. Do not talk or whisper when you are not singing in the rehearsal. Talking and whispering can be more stressful to the voice than singing.

45

even tone with leaps

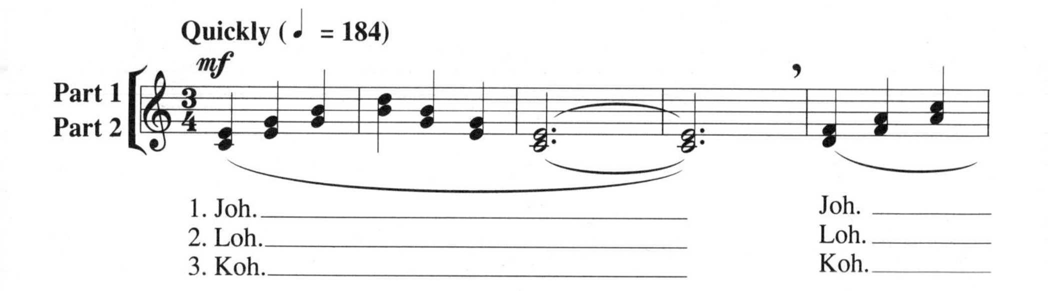
Quickly (= 184)
mf
Part 1
Part 2
1. Joh.
2. Loh.
3. Koh.
Joh.
Loh.
Koh.

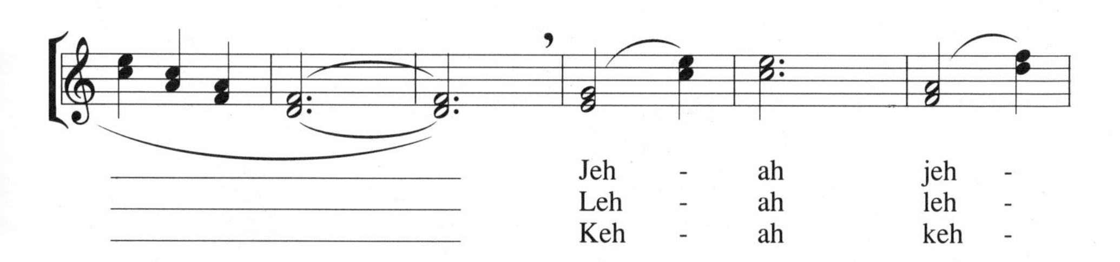
Jeh - ah jeh -
Leh - ah leh -
Keh - ah keh -

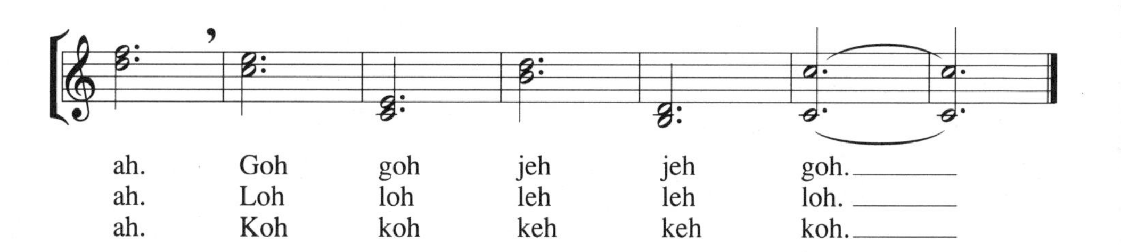
ah. Goh goh jeh jeh goh.
ah. Loh loh leh leh loh.
ah. Koh koh keh keh koh.

TIPS

A. Match the tone quality from note to note.

B. Shape the phrase as a whole, instead of singing note by note, so that the leaps are not as noticeable to the listener.

C. Sustained notes provide an opportunity to make the vowel sound as beautiful as possible.

REMINDER **Circle out of tune pitches in your concert repertoire as a reminder to listen carefully.**

46

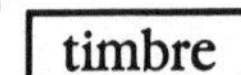
timbre

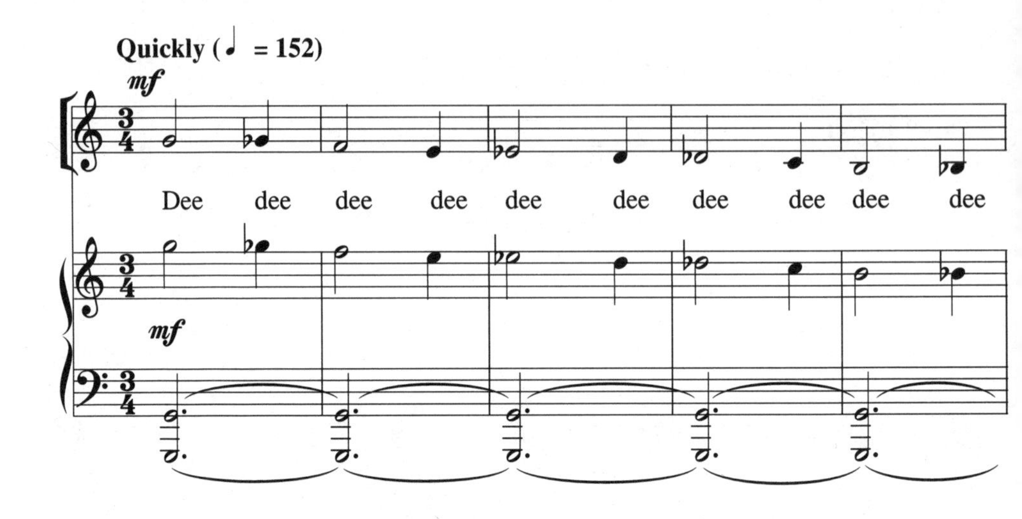
Quickly (♩ = 152)
mf
Dee dee dee dee dee dee dee dee dee dee
mf

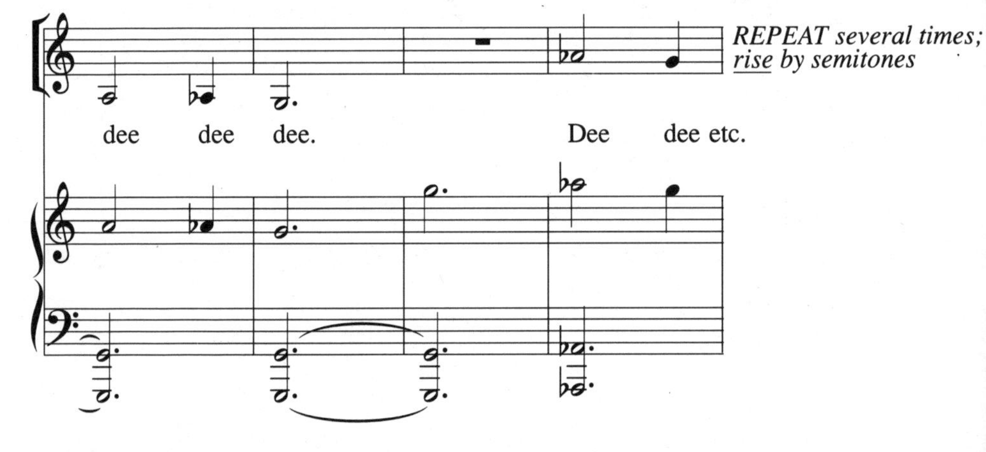
dee dee dee. Dee dee etc.
REPEAT several times; rise by semitones

TIPS

A. The timbre of your voice should fit the mood of the music. Try different timbres with this warmup:

1) Bright - think happy thoughts

2) Dark - think of black velvet

3) Cold - think of winter surrounding you

B. Keep the tuning true with each different timbre.

47

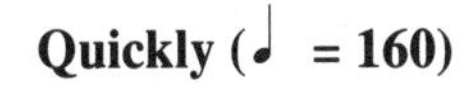
blend on high pitches

Quickly (♩ = 160)

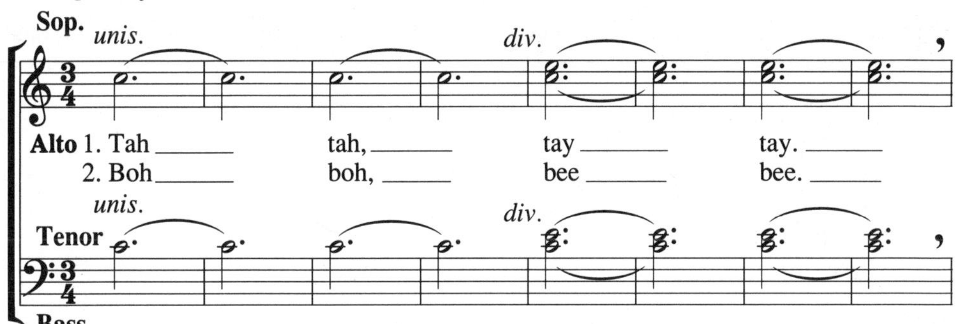
Sop.
unis.
div.
Alto 1. Tah
tah,
tay
tay.
2. Boh
boh,
bee
bee.
unis.
div.
Tenor
Bass

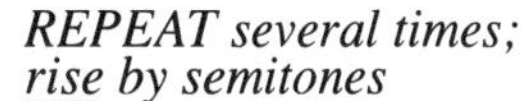
REPEAT several times;
rise by semitones

Dee-dah dee
dah
dee-dah dee
dah
day.

TIPS

A. To get a better blend, do not try to make your voice like your neighbor's. Contrasting voices can blend together to make one unified sound. You can improve the blend by using:

- **pure vowels**
- **a timbre suited to the music**
- **the same dynamic level as the rest of the choir**

correct
(all voices sounding as one):

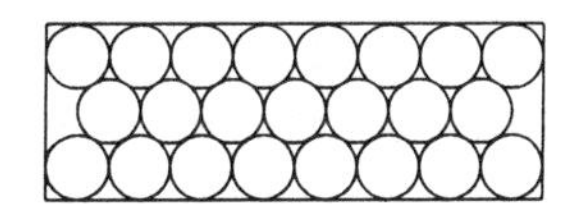

incorrect
(some voices sticking out):

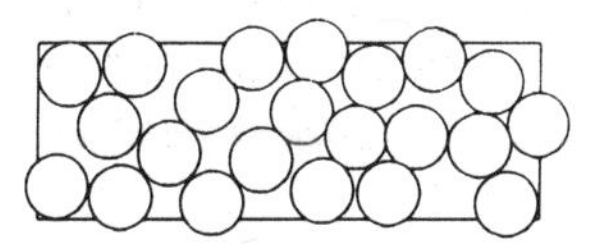

B. When the blend is good on high pitches, feel how well the voices fit together. If you are jangling with your neighbor, the blend will not be good.

48

mixed metres

Allegro (♩ = 138)
mf
How much wood could a wood-chuck chuck, could a wood-chuck
chuck? Mm yah dah dah dah dah.
How much wood could a wood - chuck chuck?
div. unis.
How_ much wood could a wood - chuck chuck?
div.
How_ much wood could a wood - chuck chuck?

TIPS

A. For rhythmic music, sing more lightly.

B. Make strong and weak pulses in your singing:

♩ = strong ♩ = weak

C. When the pitches are close together and rhythmic, your mouth should only change very slightly to move to a new pitch.

REMINDER **Flex your knees occasionally in rehearsal and in concert (between pieces).**

49

legato/staccato

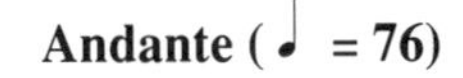
Andante (= 76)

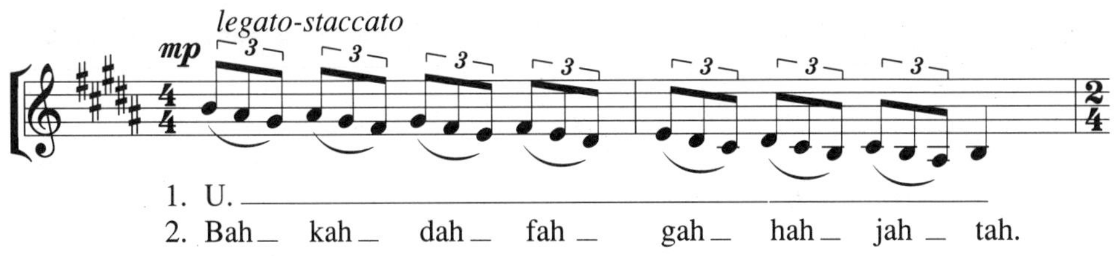
legato-staccato
mp
3
1. U.
2. Bah kah dah fah gah hah jah tah.

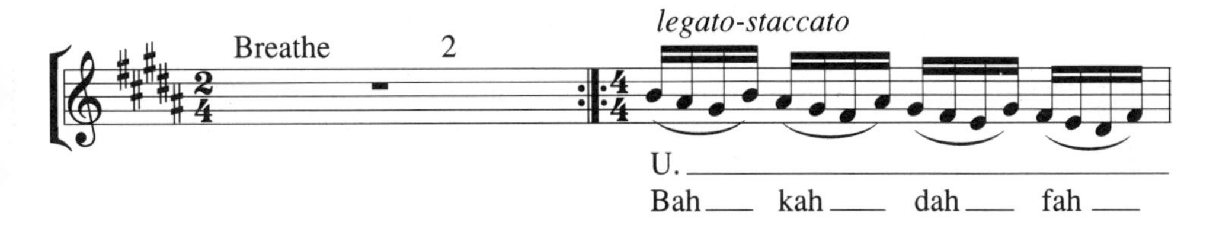
Breathe 2
legato-staccato
U.
Bah kah dah fah

gah hah jah tah.
Breathe 2
REPEAT verse 1 of entire warmup several times; rise by semitones

TIPS

A. Make sure that the first note in each grouping is secure:

3

These important structural pitches will act as a framework for the other pitches for tuning and phrasing.

B. For *legato* "u," imagine a golden thread of sound spinning out of your mouth.

C. For *staccato*, feel every cell in your body tingling.

D. For *legato*, let your body overflow with sound.

50

ornamental notes

(♩ = 132)
mp
Part 1
Mah_ boh kah roh dah kee noh.
mp
Part 2
Pah pah pah pah pah pah pah pah.
div.
Fine
Lah_ bah noh_ bah kee.
Fine
Lah see mah_ boh noh_ bah kee.
Solo Cadenza 1:
freely
D.C. al Fine
Ah
Solo Cadenza 2:
freely
D.C. al Fine
Ah

NOTE: A breath may be taken during the cadenza.

TIPS

A. The way that an ornament is performed depends on the type of music. Try these two kinds of grace notes:

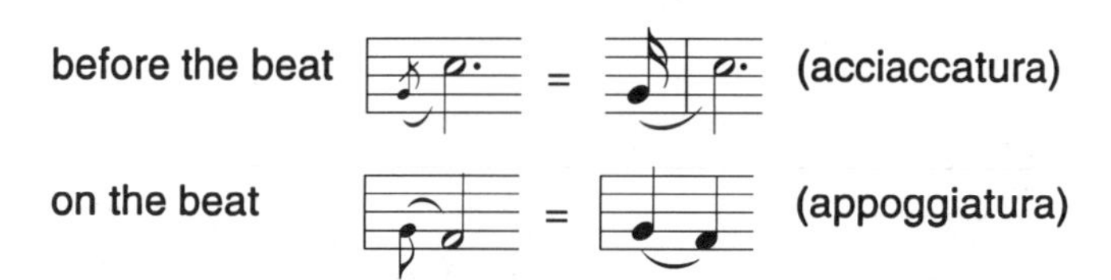
before the beat
=
(acciaccatura)
on the beat
=
(appoggiatura)

B. Usually the small notes are not as strong as the large notes.

C. Try singing the grace notes in different ways:

◆ **a catch in the throat, almost a sob**	**(Spanish)**
◆ **a light flick of sound, graceful and refined**	**(Mozart)**
◆ **"worry" the small note toward the big note, keeping full tone on the smaller note**	**(African-American)**

D. After each verse, a singer will choose a cadenza to sing solo. A cadenza is a short solo to show off the flexibility of the voice. Use rubato when you sing the cadenza solo.

51

tone cluster

NOTE: Sing all vowels as short vowels.

Quickly (♩ = 108)
Sop.
mf
div.
Ki ki ki ki ki, pa pa pa pa pa, be be be be be,
Alto
mf
Tenor
mf
div.
Ki ki ki ki ki pa pa pa pa pa, be be be be be,
Bass
mf

unis.
p
div.
tu tu tu tu tu, ki ki ki ki ki, pa pa pa pa pa,
div.
p unis.
p unis.
div.
tu tu tu tu tu, ki ki ki ki ki pa pa pa pa pa,
div.
p unis.

unis.
f
be be be be be, tu tu tu tu tu, ki ki ki ki ki,
div.
f unis.
f
be be be be be, tu tu tu tu tu, ki ki ki ki ki
f unis.

div.
unis.
pa pa pa pa pa, be be be be be, tu tu tu tu tu, tee.
div.
unis.
div.
unis.
pa pa pa pa pa, be be be be be, tu tu tu tu tu, tee.
div.
unis.

TIPS

A. When the pitches are only a semi-tone apart, the tuning must be very focused: 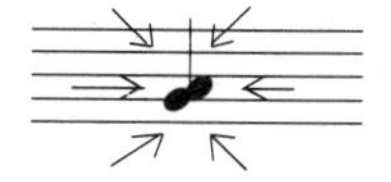

B. When another vocal part enters at a lower pitch, the higher parts should sing slightly more softly. If you cannot hear the new pitches entering, you are singing too loudly.

52

open throat

(♩ = 92)
mp
REPEAT several times;
rise by semitones
Blah blah blah blah blah;
blah blah blah blah blah.

TIPS

A. Relax your tongue. Feel your lips and cheeks "flap."

B. Raise the soft palate at the back of the top of your mouth for the final "blah" of each phrase. The back of your mouth should feel like a huge cavern.

C. When you can do this warmup with your throat wide open (and not before!), check for forward voice placement.

53

long note/short notes

Andante (♩ = 80)
mf
REPEAT several times;
rise by semitones
1. Tah tah tah tah tah.
2. Voh voh voh voh voh.
3. Veh veh veh veh veh.

TIPS

A. Practice the tuning of the first three sixteenth notes in each grouping:

tah.

B. Hear the sixteenth note pulse during the whole note:

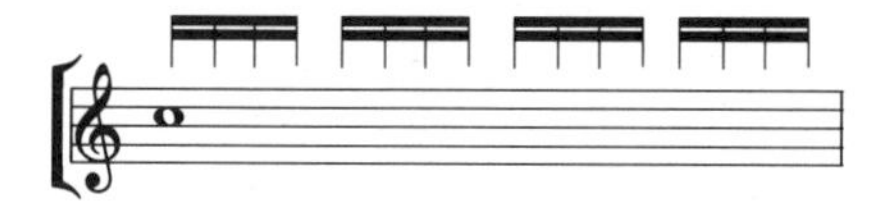

Make a slight *crescendo* at the end of the whole note to move toward the sixteenth notes in the following bar.

C. Articulate each pattern with a "t":

tah _ tah _ tah _ tah _ tah _ tah _ tah _ tah _ tah.

D. Articulate each grouping with a "v":

voh voh voh voh voh.

E. Start each grouping with a little extra emphasis:

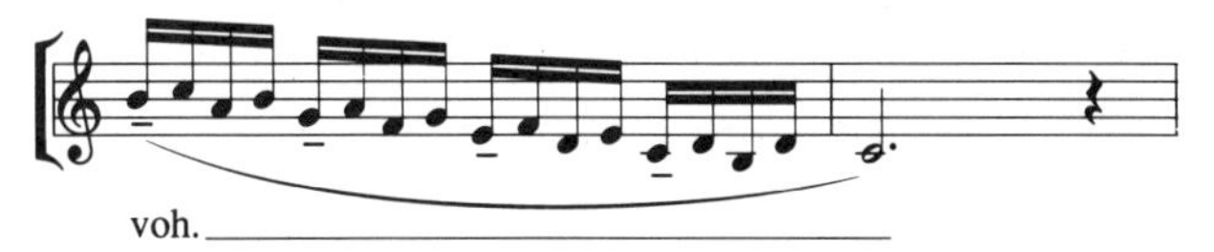
voh.

REMINDER **Open your mouth more north/south.**

54

"ing ung ong"

Slowly (♩ = 76)
mp
King of the sing-ing,
Where have you sung songs?

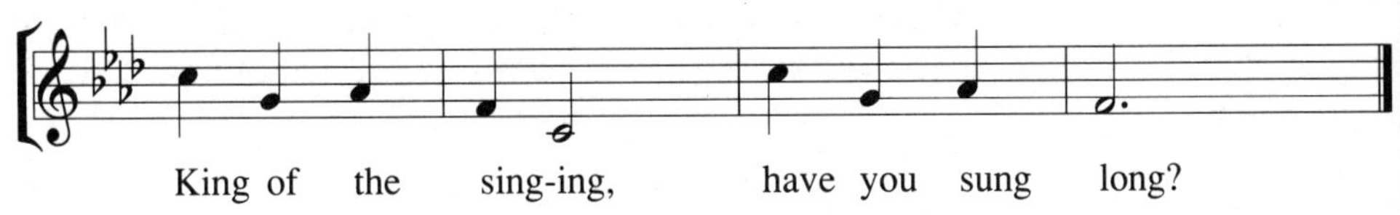
King of the sing-ing,
have you sung long?

TIPS

A. "Ng" does not project very well. If you close down too soon to the "ng," the phrase will be broken by a blank moment in the sound.

B. Always use lots of resonance on the short vowels before "ng." This helps to keep the sound open.

C. "Of" is pronounced "ahv."

55

phrases broken internally by rests

Quickly (♩ = 144)
Part 1
Part 2
mp
div.
There was a bi - cy - cle_ up - on a crook-ed lane_
dodg-ing the chick-ens
unis.
fly - ing by. There was a
div.
bi - cy - cle___ up - on a
unis.
crook-ed lane._

TIPS

A. Do not breathe during every rest.

B. Shape the entire phrase, not just a fragment of it:

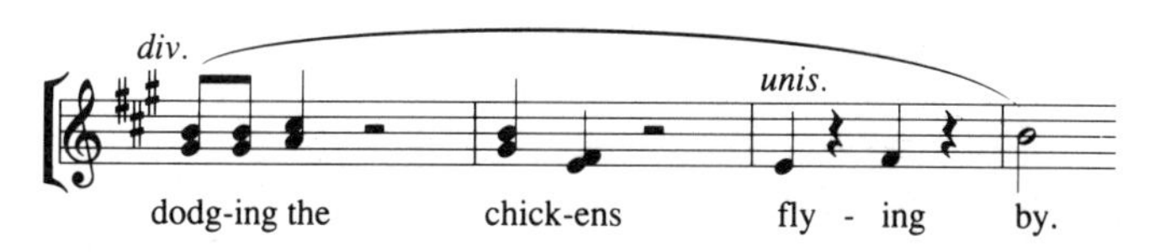
div.
unis.
dodg-ing the chick-ens fly - ing by.

C. Feel the music continue inside you during each rest.

D. Make sure the dropping sounds are not flat:

crook<u>ed</u> dodg<u>ing</u> chick<u>ens</u> fly<u>ing</u>

REMINDER **Drink plenty of water every day.**

56

dropping sounds on rising pitches

Andante (♩ = 88)
unis. mf
Part 1
Part 2
Ev-'ry riv-er has some wa-ter; ev-'ry

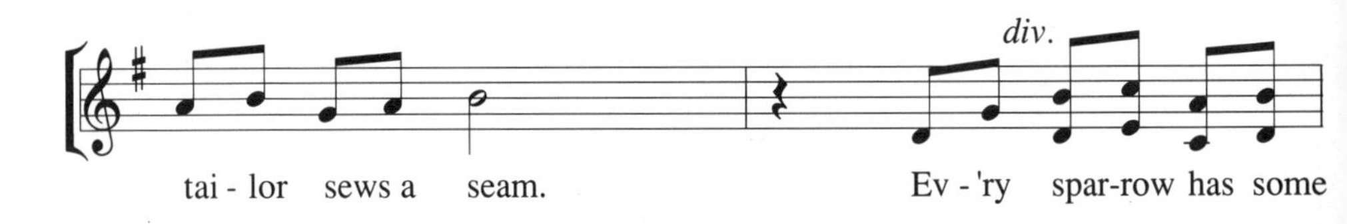
div.
tai-lor sews a seam. Ev-'ry spar-row has some

feath-ers: ev-'ry per-son has a dream.

TIPS

A. In some types of music, you need to relax the dynamics on the second of each pair of notes:

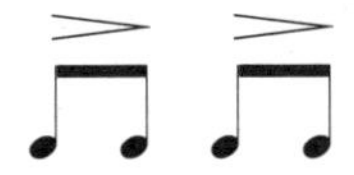

This may help the flow of the rhythms or may help to place the emphasis on the important syllables of the lyrics.

B. Check the tuning of the second pitch in each grouping.

57

matching timbre for octaves

Quickly (♩ = 144)
REPEAT several times; rise by semitones
mf
etc.
1. Mee mah
2. Mah mee

TIPS

A. Use the pressure from your tummy to sing the octave leap.

B. Match the resonance for the leap.

C. Keep up the quality to the end of each phrase.

D. Match the color (bright/dark) for the leap.

58

dim. in ascending passage

(♩ = 76)
U

Ee
etc.
REPEAT, rising by semitones

TIPS

A. As the music gets higher and softer:

i) Use a smaller focus;

ii) Sing more lightly.

B. Make the music sound more and more exciting as it softens.

C. Give the tone some depth on the *dim.* so that it will not sound too thin.

59

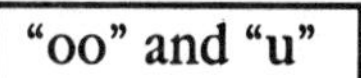
“oo” and “u”

(♩ = 63)
unis.
mf
Part 1
Part 2
Good news, good news, Bring the lute and
div.
harp, Hal - le - lu - ia! Good news, Hal - le -
lu - ia; Good news, Hal - le - lu - ia! Good news,
good news; good news, good news!

TIPS

A. For the “oo” in “good,” round your lips and project them slightly forward.

B. For “news” and “lute,” pronounce the vowel the same as the name of the letter “u” is pronounced (yu):

nyuz not *nuz*
lyut not *lut*

Go through the “y” sound very quickly.

C. Sometimes an “s” is pronounced as a “z”:

news = nyuz

60

climax

Slowly (♩ = 96)
mp
I can see yes - ter - day.
I re -mem-ber the

young days. While lov - ers wan - der by the

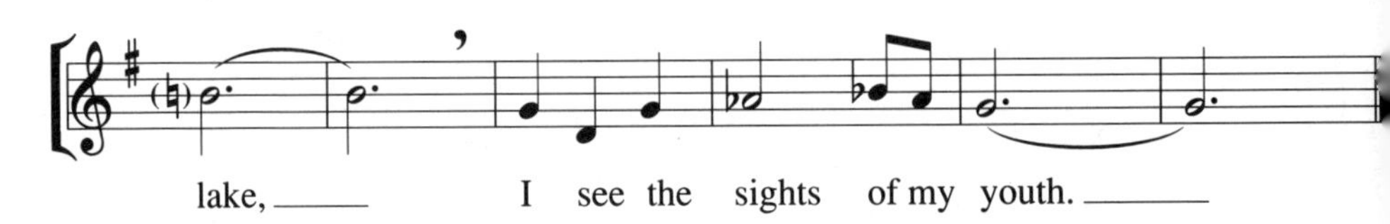
lake, I see the sights of my youth.

TIPS

Practice shaping the climax in different ways:

A. **Lean into the pitches which are dissonant with the G major harmonies (Eb, Bb, Ab). Then relax the tone and volume when the dissonance resolves.**

B. **Drive the music intensely toward the climax of each phrase:**

C. **Let the suspense build slowly as the music gently rolls toward the climax:**

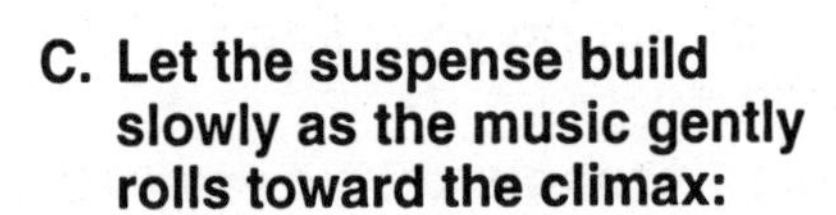

D. **Build the excitement higher and higher; then ease off just before the climax of each phrase so that there is the feeling that you have been swept off your feet at the climax:**

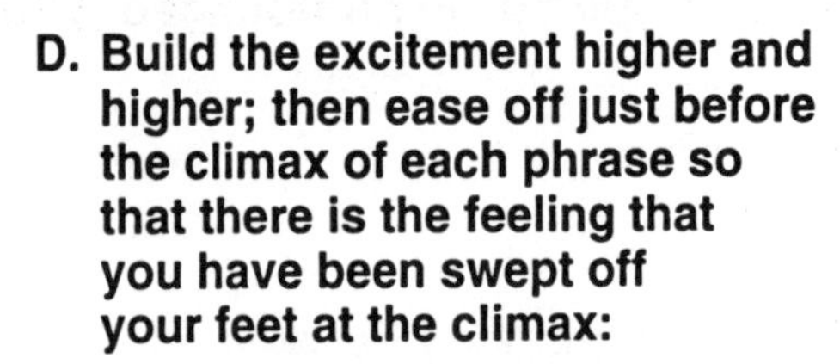

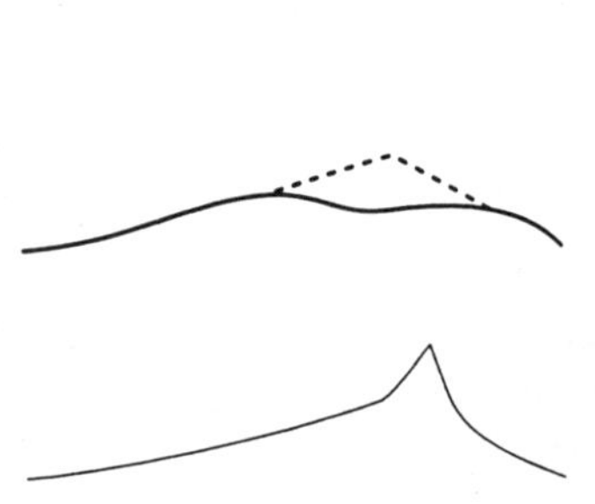

E. **Use a dramatic "smash" at the high point of each climax:**

61

melismas with some longer notes

Andante (♩ = 92)
G.F. Handel
mf
Part 1
A - - - men.
mf
Part 2
A - - men, A - men.

TIPS

A Let your top front teeth help to make the "ah" sparkle.

B. Warm up the tone on the longer pitches within the melisma.

C. Match the lower pitches with the quality of the higher pitches.

D. Imagine the sixteenth notes coming from the nape of your neck (the small spot on the back of your head where the hair meets the bare skin of your neck):

62

fermata

𝄐 = fermata = hold this note until the conductor moves on

Quickly (♩ = 144)
unis. mp
Part 1
Part 2
1. Mee-nah mee-nah mee-nah mah moh mu.
2. Mee-nah mee-nah mee-nah meet a moose.

Mee-nah mee-nah mee-nah mah moh mu.
Mee-nah mee-nah mee-nah meet a moose.

div. mf
Mee-nah mee-nah mee-nah mah ah ah ah.
Mee-nah mee-nah mee-nah mah ah ah ah.

TIPS

A. Keep the energy in the tone during each fermata.

B. Think of something funny as you sing the notes with fermatas. This helps to keep the tone sound more relaxed and alive.

rhythmic patterns with accents

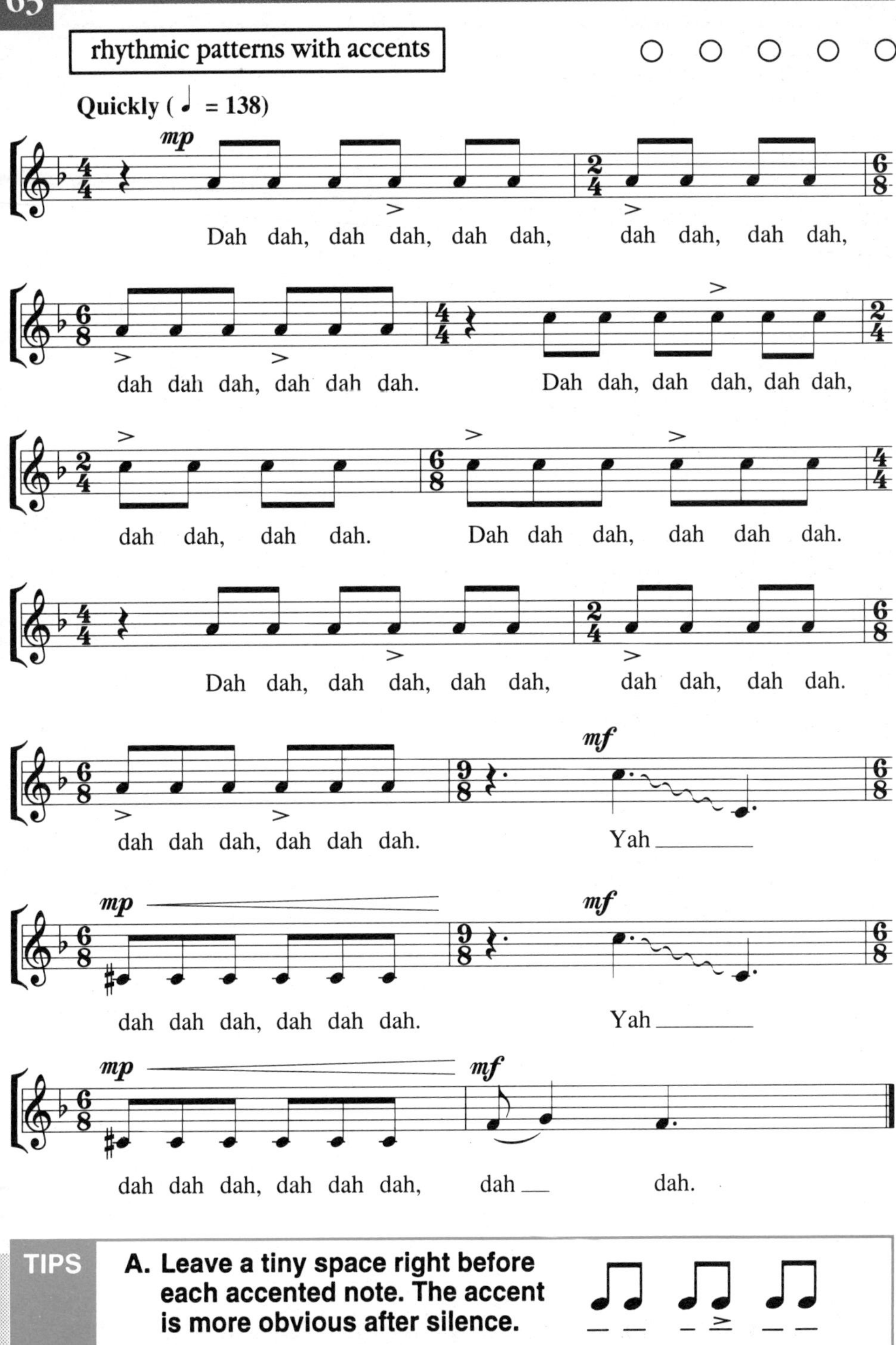
Quickly (♩ = 138)
mp
Dah dah, dah dah, dah dah, dah dah, dah dah,
dah dah dah, dah dah dah. Dah dah, dah dah, dah dah,
dah dah, dah dah. Dah dah dah, dah dah dah.
Dah dah, dah dah, dah dah, dah dah, dah dah.
mf
dah dah dah, dah dah dah. Yah
mp
mf
dah dah dah, dah dah dah. Yah
mp
mf
dah dah dah, dah dah dah, dah dah.

TIPS

A. Leave a tiny space right before each accented note. The accent is more obvious after silence.

B. Make sure that the tuning is not distorted on the accents.

64

blend on low pitches

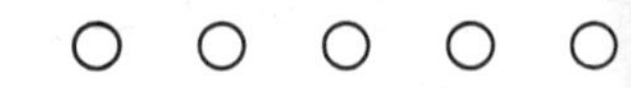

Adagio (♩ = 76)
Sop. mf
Alto
Wait and watch for the new world is
Tenor mf
Bass
Wait and watch for the new world is

wait - ing. Wipe_ your tears a - way.
wait - ing. Wipe your_ tears a - way.

TIPS

A. If your voice is disturbing the blend, determine why it stands out and correct the problem.

B. Think of your vocal section as being one single person with a single quality of sound — a blended mixture of all the different types of voices.

C. The consonant should be sung a fraction of a second before the beat:

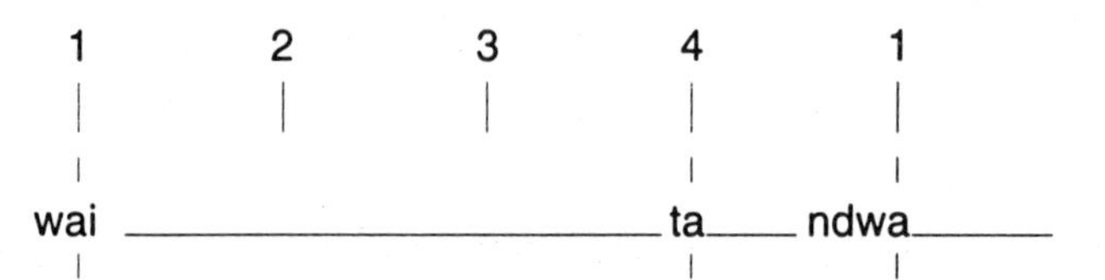
1 2 3 4 1
wai ta ndwa

"W" is formed by the glide of the lips but it should be a very fast glide.

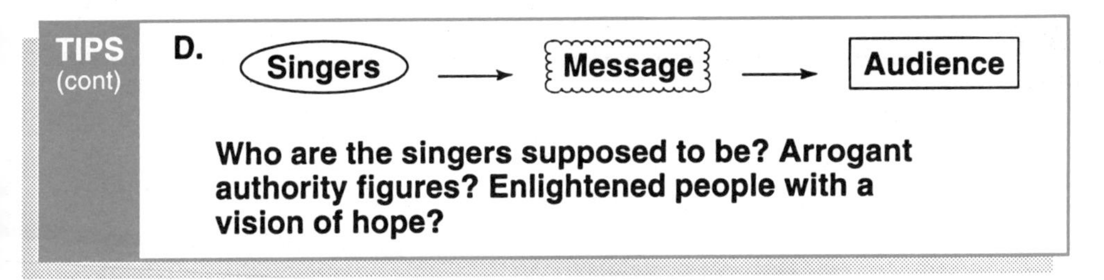
TIPS
(cont)
D.
Singers
Message
Audience
Who are the singers supposed to be? Arrogant authority figures? Enlightened people with a vision of hope?

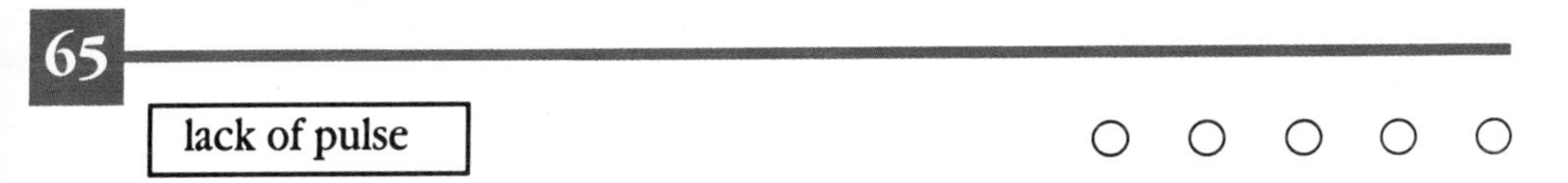
65
lack of pulse

Each singer chooses a different tempo. Keep repeating each verse until conductor's cue for next verse.

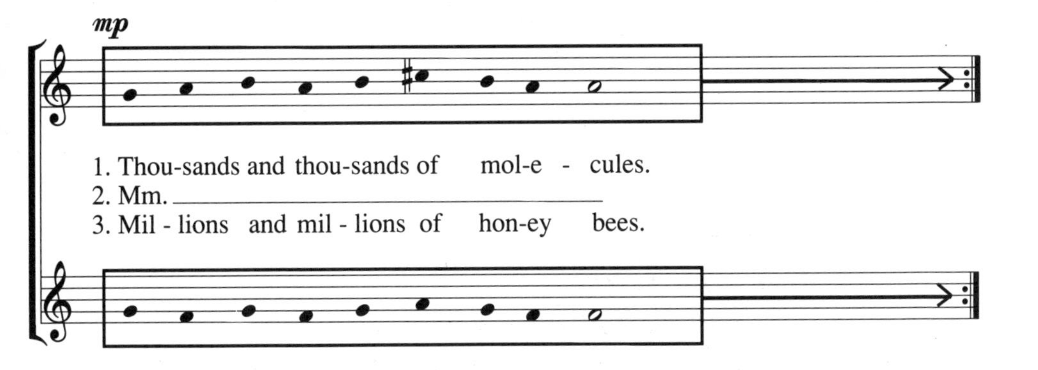
mp
1. Thou-sands and thou-sands of mol-e - cules.
2. Mm.
3. Mil - lions and mil - lions of hon-ey bees.

TIPS

A. **Some music requires a sense of timelessness. Sing without an even beat. Let the music float from note to note. Repeat the phrase differently each time.**

B. **Imagine that you are walking along a beach but you leave no footprints in the sand. There is no weight to the movement of your feet; no weight to the notes in the music.**

66

ff; declamatory

Maestoso (♩ = 60)
ff
Part 1
Part 2
The time has come.
REPEAT several times; rise by semitones

TIPS

A. ** Multiple Choice **

***ff* means:**

a) Blastissimo;

b) Nail the audience to the wall;

c) Sound like you ate raw meat for lunch;

(d) Feel the vibrations in the soles of your feet;

(e) Use your whole body for a full, rich sound.

B. A declamatory style is often used in loud passages of oratorio music. Emphasize <u>every</u> word by singing like royalty who are accustomed to making declarations of great authority to the entire kingdom.

67

the less important words

Moderato (♩ = 120)
Sop.
mp
Alto
The lit - tle things in life can be the things that make all ___ the
mp
Tenor
Bass

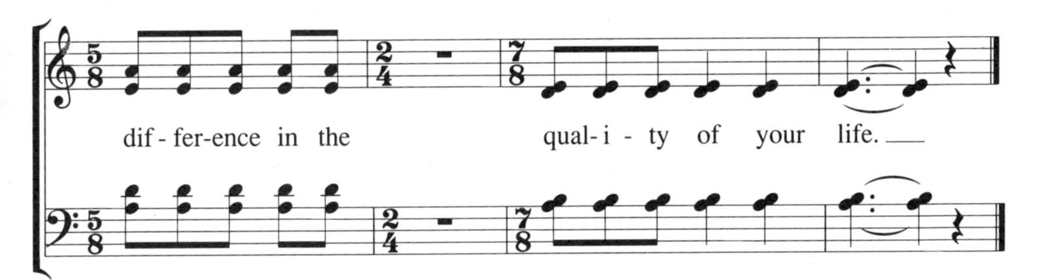
dif - fer-ence in the qual- i - ty of your life. ___

TIPS

A. Check the most important words first. Are you emphasizing the strong syllables?

B. Be aware of the short words (e.g. the, a, of) which are less important for the meaning of the lyrics but are important for the continuity of the line and for the overall clarity of sound.

C. Check the less important words for:

1) Purity of vowel sound (e.g. the = thah);

2) Tuning;

3) Duration — are the vowels stretched out?

D. If a phrase begins with a less important word, automatically make it sound a bit more important because the entry word is always given priority.

68

slurred leaps

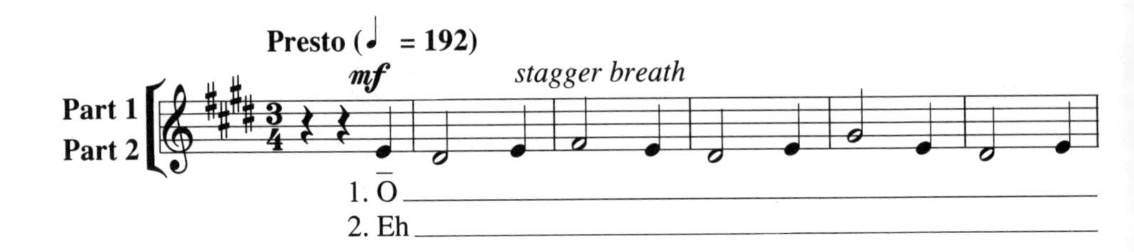
Presto (♩ = 192)
mf
stagger breath
Part 1
Part 2
1. O
2. Eh

Ah
Ee

TIPS

- **A. Stagger breathe before you start to lose momentum.**
- **B. Let the sound bounce up on each leap.**
- **C. Imagine a trampoline is bouncing you up. Land lightly on your feet.**
- **D. Make the bounce smooth (*legato*).**

69

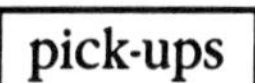
pick-ups

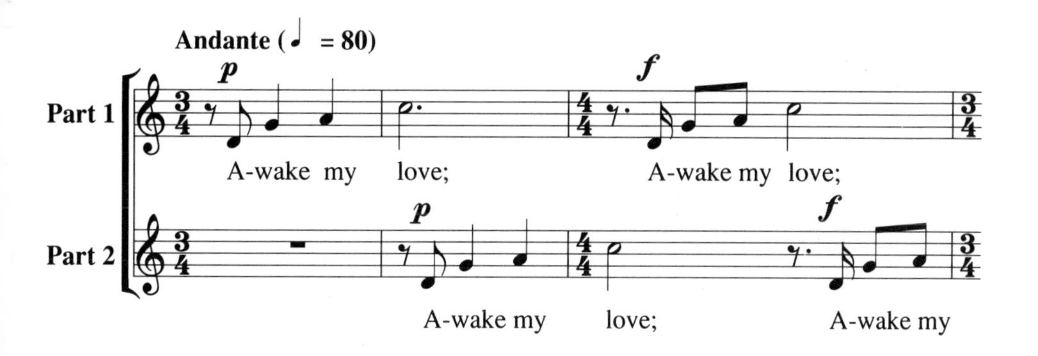
Andante (♩ = 80)
Part 1
Part 2
p
f
A-wake my love; A-wake my love;
A-wake my love; A-wake my

mf
Be read-y for the dawn. A - rise! The
love. Be read-y for the dawn. A - rise!

dawn is nigh.
The dawn is nigh.

TIPS

A. Feel the strong beat on the rest. Then let the eighth note entry bounce in after the rest.

B. For the sixteenth note entry, feel the subdivision of the beat as you breathe in:

A - wake, my love

C. Follow the terraced dynamics.

D. For a more *legato* entry:

i) Let the eighth note enter more gently.

ii) Join the sixteenth note entry smoothly to the rest of the phrase.

70

whole tone scale

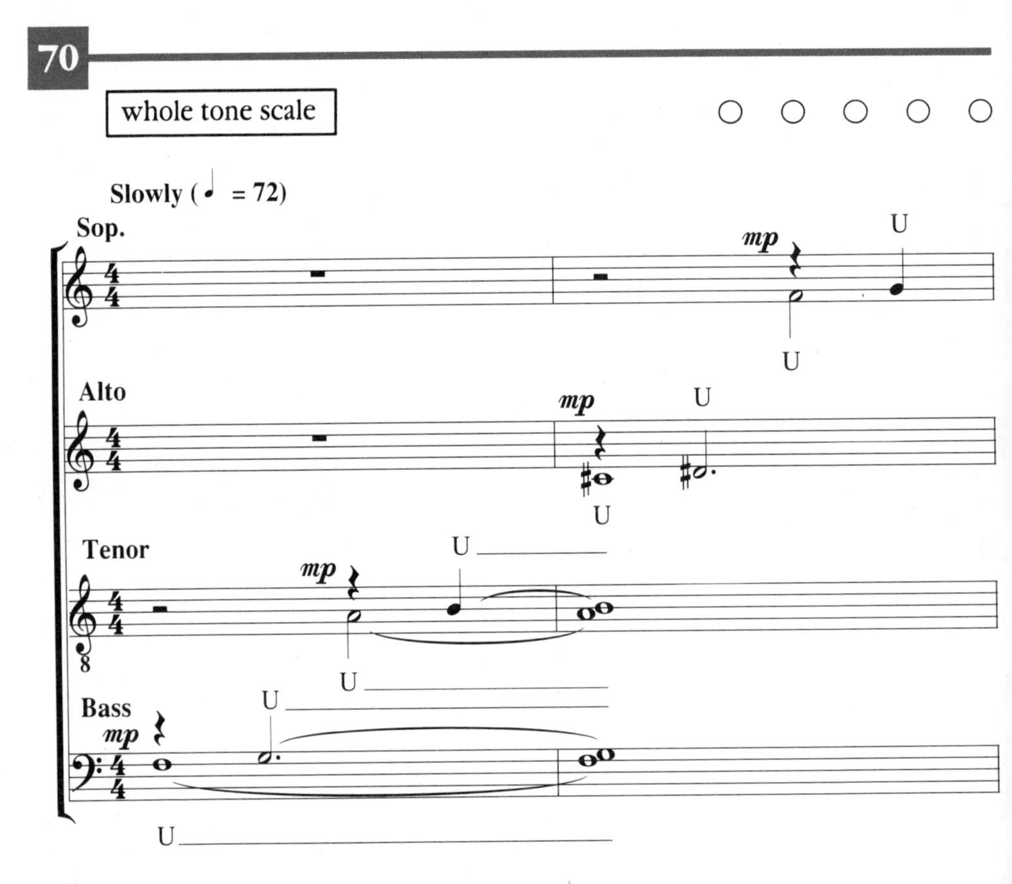
Slowly (♩ = 72)
Sop.
Alto
Tenor
Bass
mp
U

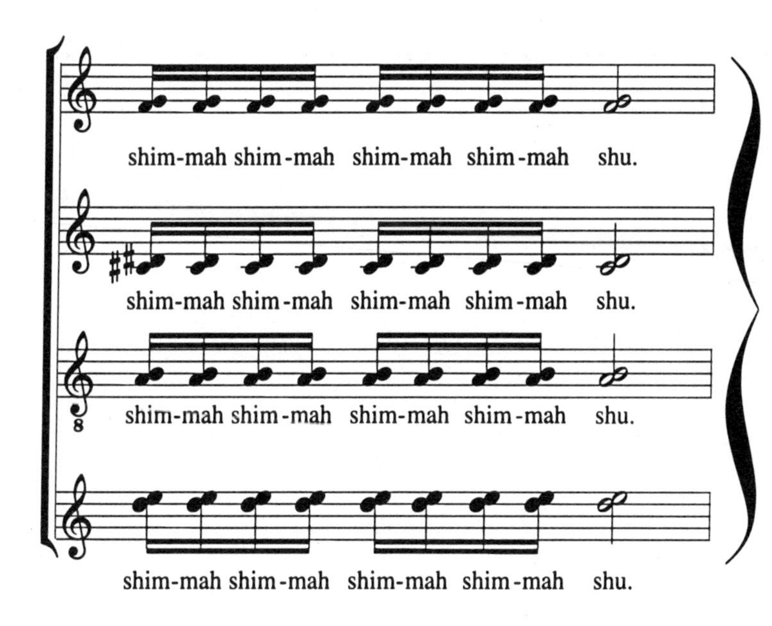
shim-mah shim-mah shim-mah shim-mah shu.
shim-mah shim-mah shim-mah shim-mah shu.
shim-mah shim-mah shim-mah shim-mah shu.
shim-mah shim-mah shim-mah shim-mah shu.
8

REPEAT warmup twice, each time starting a whole tone higher

TIPS

A. Breathe early and start precisely in time.

B. Keep the tuning steady on the rhythmic part.

71

entry on a high note

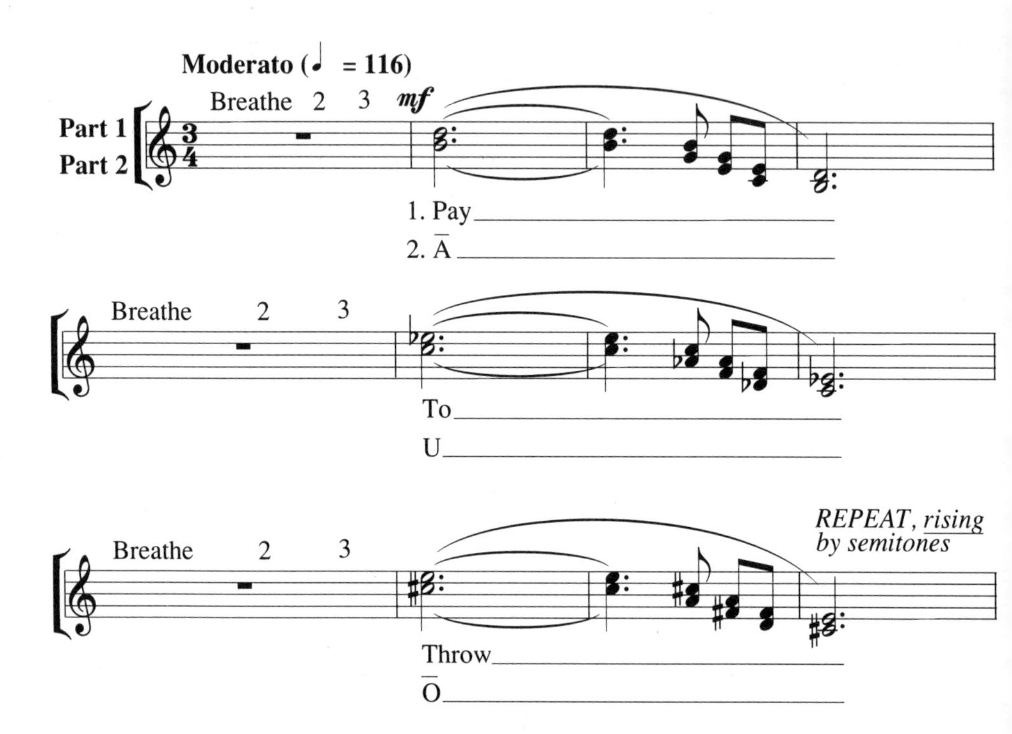
Moderato (♩ = 116)
Part 1
Part 2
Breathe 2 3 mf
1. Pay
2. Ā
Breathe 2 3
To
U
Breathe 2 3
Throw
Ō
REPEAT, rising by semitones

TIPS

A. Hear the sound in your mind before you begin.

B. Shape your mouth for a beautiful tone as you inhale slowly.

C. If the high pitch begins with a vowel, inhale as if you were singing that vowel at the right pitch level. Then sing out.

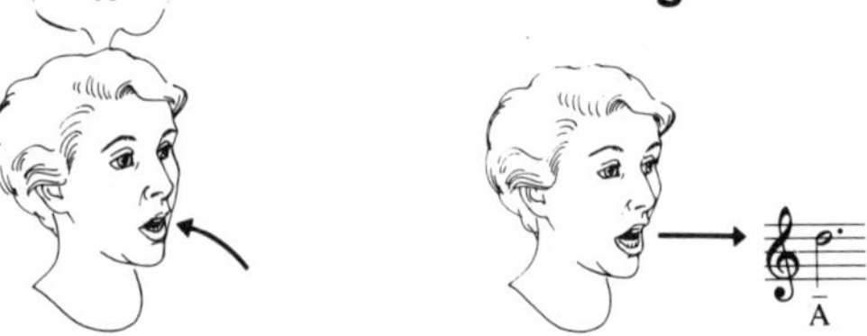
A
A

D. Continue with your best quality throughout the long note.

72

final vowel/initial vowel

(♩ = 104)
mf
Be a, why is, say ev-'ry, do each, go a - way.
Be a, why is, say ev-'ry, do each, go a - way.
Be a, why is, say ev - 'ry, do each, go a - way.

TIPS

A. Do not add a glide between the vowels:

bee ah not *beeyah* *du eech* not *duweech*

B. The second vowel should be distinct. Leave a small space between the words and emphasize the beginning of the second word.

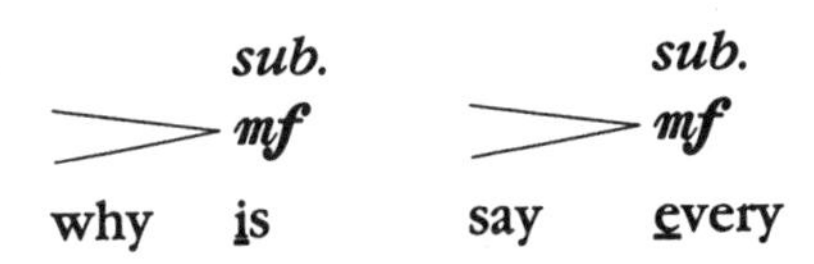
sub.
mf
why is
sub.
mf
say every

73

colors

(♩ = 104)
mp
Part 1
Flow.
mp
Part 2
Jā mā yoh ja mā
yoh ja mā yoh.
Jā mā yoh jā mā yoh
Flow.
jā mā yoh.
Jā mā flow yoh.
Jā mā flow yoh.

TIP

Try singing this warmup while you imagine one of these colors:

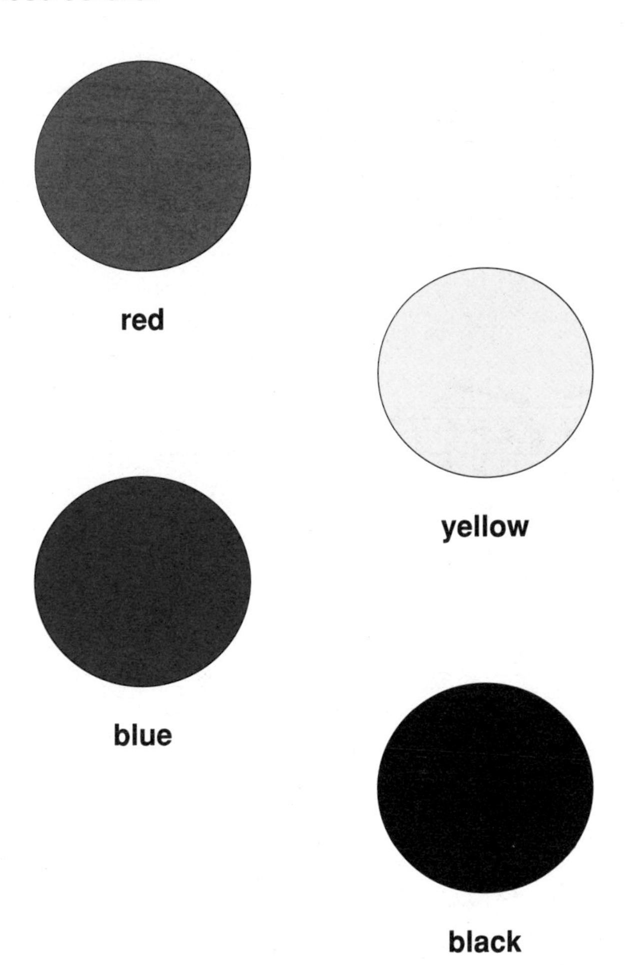
red
yellow
blue
black

Notice how the timbre of your voice changes for each color. The music will not necessarily sound "red" or "yellow," but your reaction to the color can change the sound in some slight way.

74

imaging to save the voice

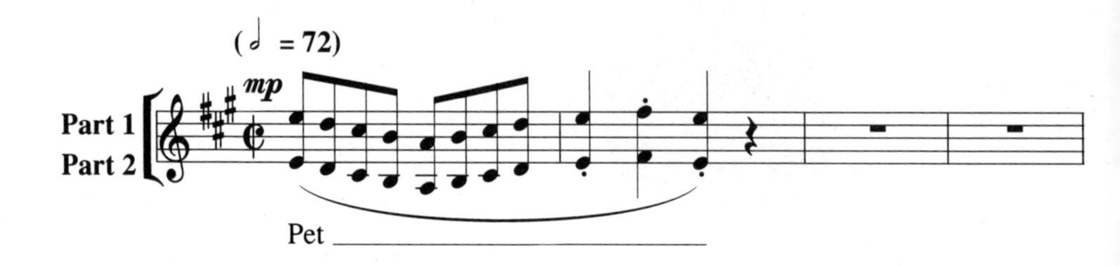

(𝅗𝅥 = 72)
mp
Part 1
Part 2
Pet

Pit

Put

Pat

TIPS

A. During the rests, practice the previous phrase silently in your mind.

B. Intensive practice with a very high or low tessitura can be stressful for the voice. With silent singing, you can mentally practice the skills you need but you are not wearing out your voice at the same time.

FOURTH YEAR PROGRESS CHART

CIRCLE the appropriate number:

1 - understands the skill
2 - can do the skill
3 - some improvement shown
4 - good progress
5 - excellent progress
6 - remembers consistently

Singers in Position - stand like a VIP	1 2 3 4 5 6
- suspend your head from a thread	1 2 3 4 5 6
38. articulated hiss	1 2 3 4 5 6
39. even resonance	1 2 3 4 5 6
40. rubato	1 2 3 4 5 6
- avoid noise pollution	1 2 3 4 5 6
41. range extension down	1 2 3 4 5 6
Quick Check - Early morning hum	1 2 3 4 5 6
42. *cresc. dim.*	1 2 3 4 5 6
43. long *legato* phrasing	1 2 3 4 5 6
- be aware of contrary motion	1 2 3 4 5 6
44. final consonant/initial consonant	1 2 3 4 5 6
Pacing Your Voice -	1 2 3 4 5 6
45. even tone with leaps	1 2 3 4 5 6
- circle out of tune pitches	1 2 3 4 5 6
46. timbre	1 2 3 4 5 6
47. blend on high pitches	1 2 3 4 5 6
48. mixed metres	1 2 3 4 5 6
- use strong and weak pulses	1 2 3 4 5 6
49. *legato/staccato*	1 2 3 4 5 6
50. ornamental notes	1 2 3 4 5 6
Quick check: Drinking water?	1 2 3 4 5 6
51. tone cluster	1 2 3 4 5 6
52. open throat - soft palate up	1 2 3 4 5 6
53. long note/short notes	1 2 3 4 5 6
- articulating sixteenth notes	1 2 3 4 5 6
54. "ing ung ong"	1 2 3 4 5 6
55. phrases broken internally by rests	1 2 3 4 5 6
- tune dropping sounds	1 2 3 4 5 6

56. dropping sounds on rising pitches	1 2 3 4 5 6
57. matching timbre for octaves	1 2 3 4 5 6
58. *dim.* in ascending passage	1 2 3 4 5 6
Quick check: Posture?	1 2 3 4 5 6
59. "oo" and "u"	1 2 3 4 5 6
60. climax	1 2 3 4 5 6
- lean into dissonance	1 2 3 4 5 6
- drive toward climax	1 2 3 4 5 6
- gently roll toward climax	1 2 3 4 5 6
- ease off just before climax	1 2 3 4 5 6
- dramatic "smash" at climax	1 2 3 4 5 6
61. melismas with some longer notes	1 2 3 4 5 6
62. fermata	1 2 3 4 5 6
63. rhythmic patterns with accents	1 2 3 4 5 6
64. blend on low pitches	1 2 3 4 5 6
- using a role to communicate to audience	1 2 3 4 5 6
65. lack of pulse	1 2 3 4 5 6
66. *ff*	1 2 3 4 5 6
- declamatory	1 2 3 4 5 6
67. the less important words	1 2 3 4 5 6
68. slurred leaps	1 2 3 4 5 6
Quick check: Breathing?	1 2 3 4 5 6
69. pick-ups	1 2 3 4 5 6
70. whole tone scale	1 2 3 4 5 6
71. entry on a high note	1 2 3 4 5 6
72. final vowel/initial vowel	1 2 3 4 5 6
73. colors	1 2 3 4 5 6
74. imaging to save voice	1 2 3 4 5 6

◆ ◆ **CONGRATULATIONS!** ◆ ◆

Index